Rigging and Lifting Principles

AMERICAN TECHNICAL PUBLISHERS
ORLAND PARK, ILLINOIS 60467-5756

IN PARTNERSHIP WITH NJATC

American Technical Publishers, Inc., Editorial Staff

Editor in Chief:
        Jonathan F. Gosse
Vice President—Production:
        Peter A. Zurlis
Art Manager:
        James M. Clarke
Technical Editor:
        Julie M. Welch
Copy Editor:
        Jeana M. Platz
Cover Design:
        James M. Clarke
Illustration/Layout:
        Melanie G. Doornbos
        Eric T. Comiza

Dacron is a registered trademark of Invista North America. Kevlar and Teflon are registered trademarks of E. I. Du Pont de Nemours and Company Corporation. Monel is a registered trademark of Inco Alloys International, Inc.

1 2 3 4 5 6 7 8 9 – 10 – 9 8 7 6 5 4 3 2 1

Printed in the United States of America

        ISBN 978-0-8269-3648-6

 This book is printed on recycled paper.

 3-S

Rigging and Lifting Principles

Acknowledgments

The publisher is grateful to the following for providing photographs and technical assistance:

The Crosby Group, Inc.
Harrington Hoists, Inc.
Ingersoll-Rand Material Handling
Lift-All Company, Inc.
Ratcliff Hoist Co.
Wick Homes

Tom Bowes
    Detroit Electrical Industry Training Center

Contents

Introduction

Rigging and Lifting Principles is an introduction to the fundamental concepts involved in preparing and lifting loads with hoisting equipment. Rigging and lifting are common activities at construction sites, manufacturing plants, and industrial facilities for moving loads and equipment. The lifting and moving of large loads is potentially very dangerous, so all personnel involved must have the proper training and experience.

This textbook focuses on rigging equipment, general rigging practices, and the associated calculations that involve weight, forces, and angles. Calculations can be critical to maintaining a controlled lift with the proper margin of safety. The particular lifting application must be considered carefully as certain factors can significantly affect the equipment requirements.

The topics presented in this textbook include weight and balance, sling hitch configurations, sling types, rigging hardware, safety factors, equipment inspection, hoists, and cranes. Each chapter begins with an introduction to the topic and chapter objectives to be achieved when studying the material. Each concept is reinforced with practical examples. Numerous full-color illustrations and photographs depict best practices and common applications. Additional tips and safety reminders are included throughout as boxed notes. *Rigging and Lifting Principles* provides a solid foundation of safe material handling practices that complements the instruction in hands-on training programs.

ATPeResources.com provides access to additional technical content and a list of Internet links to manufacturer, organization, government, and ATP resources. The American Technical Publishers web site (www.go2atp.com) includes information on related training products.

The Publisher

Rigging 1

In the course of construction, material deliveries, equipment installation, and other activities, loads must be properly rigged and safely lifted to their final destination. These jobs require a thorough understanding of many topics, including the calculation of various weights and forces. The determination of load weight and balance is critical to maintaining control of a load while lifting. Different types of eyebolts are used as lift points for various applications. Slings are a primary rigging component that can be arranged in several different ways to support a load. The arrangement of lift points and slings affects the forces and stress they experience, which must be kept to a minimum.

Objectives

- Describe the importance of weight and balance when rigging and lifting.
- Calculate a load's weight and estimate its center of gravity.
- Differentiate between types of eyebolts and their use.
- Evaluate the load capacities of eyebolts in different applications.
- Compare the types of sling hitches.
- Calculate the forces experienced by slings used at angles other than vertical.

WEIGHT AND BALANCE

Rigging is the securing of loads with the proper equipment and arrangement in preparation for lifting. Rigging involves choosing the appropriate components to support the load weight, attaching them to the lifting equipment, and arranging them properly to balance the load. *Lifting* is the hoisting of loads by mechanical means. Rigging and lifting activities also involve planning the controlled movement of loads to avoid damage or safety hazards. All phases of a rigging and lifting job must be planned out prior to beginning the job.

The primary concerns of planning a lift are determining the weight and determining the balance of the load. Other considerations include the load shape, path of travel, location (indoor or outdoor), and landing areas. Sometimes, the conditions of the lift change as the load is moved and positioned.

Load Weight

The most critical factor in rigging and lifting is the weight of a load. The weight must be known prior to planning the lift in order to select the proper rigging and hoisting equipment and determine the required safety measures. Each component must be rated for at least its portion of the weight of the load. The weakest component determines the strength of the entire lifting system. **See Figure 1-1.**

The weight of the load is sometimes found on equipment data plates, shipping documents, or the manufacturer's product information. Always ensure that the weight has not changed since the documentation was prepared. Weight may be greater if the load has been modified or remains in a container or jig.

If a specified load weight is unavailable, it can be calculated using stock material weight tables or area, volume, and material weight information. To obtain the full-load weight, the weight of the rigging equipment is added to the total load weight.

Stock Material Weight Tables. Stock material weight tables are used when a load consists of common stock or structural shapes, such as round and square bars, round and square tubing, I-beams, angles, tees, channels, and plates. These shapes may be available in various steels, aluminum, copper, brass, or other materials. Stock material weight tables list the weight of materials by their linear, area, or volumetric measurements, in either the English or metric systems. Tables for common shapes and sizes are readily available in material reference books or manufacturer literature. **See Figure 1-2. See Appendix.** For example, a 1″ diameter, round steel bar weighs 2.67 lb/ft.

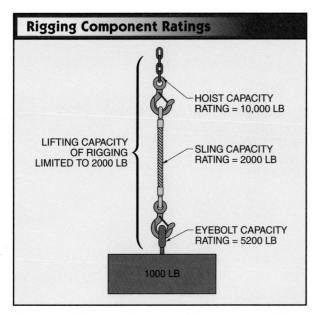

Figure 1-1. The capacity rating of the weakest individual components in a rigging arrangement determines the lifting capacity of the whole arrangement.

Weight of Steel Stock Materials			
Diameter or Thickness*	Round Bar†	Square Bar†	Sheet/Plate‡
1/16	—	—	2.55
1/8	0.0417	0.0531	5.11
3/16	0.0939	0.120	7.66
1/4	0.167	0.213	10.2
3/8	0.376	0.478	15.3
1/2	0.668	0.850	20.4
3/4	1.50	1.91	30.6
1	2.67	3.40	40.8
1 1/4	4.17	5.31	51.1
1 1/2	6.01	7.65	61.3
1 3/4	8.18	10.4	71.5
2	10.7	13.6	81.7
4	42.7	54.4	163
6	96.1	122	245

* in in.
† in lb/ft
‡ in lb/sqft

Figure 1-2. Stock material weight tables list the weights of common construction shapes per linear or area unit.

The weight of linear stock material is calculated by applying the following formula:

$$W_{total} = n \times l \times W_l$$
where
W_{total} = total weight (in lb)
n = number of pieces
l = length (in ft)
W_l = linear unit weight (in lb/ft)

For example, what is the total material weight of a bundle of 150 pieces of 10′ long, ½″ diameter steel EMT conduit? *Note:* A steel EMT conduit at ½″ weighs 0.30 lb/ft.

$$W_{total} = n \times l \times W_l$$
$$W_{total} = 150 \times 10 \times 0.30$$
$$W_{total} = \textbf{450 lb}$$

Load weights of plates or sheets are calculated by multiplying the material unit weight (from stock material weight tables) by the number of plates or sheets and their area. The weight of plate or sheet stock material is calculated by applying the following formula:

$$W_{total} = n \times l \times w \times W_A$$
where
W_{total} = total weight (in lb)
n = number of pieces
l = length (in ft)
w = width (in ft)
W_A = area unit weight (in lb/sq ft)

For example, what is the total material weight of a load consisting of 35 pieces of 4′ × 8′ steel sheet ¹⁄₁₆″ thick? *Note:* A steel sheet at ¹⁄₁₆″ thick weighs 2.55 lb/sq ft.

$$W_{total} = n \times l \times w \times W_A$$
$$W_{total} = 35 \times 8 \times 4 \times 2.55$$
$$W_{total} = \textbf{2856 lb}$$

Material Weight Calculations. If a load does not consist of stock shapes and total weight information is not otherwise available, the load weight can be calculated from the load's area and/or volume based on measurements of its actual dimensions. If the load is made from relatively thin plate or sheet stock, its total surface area is multiplied by the area unit weight of the plate or sheet, which is found in a stock material weight table. If the load is made from thick, solid parts, its total volume is multiplied by the material's volume unit weight (density), which can also be found in a stock material weight table. **See Figure 1-3.** These calculations are represented by the following formulas:

$$W_{total} = A \times W_A$$
or
$$W_{total} = V \times W_V$$
where
W_{total} = total weight (in lb)
A = total surface area (in sq ft)
W_A = area unit weight (in lb/sq ft)
V = total volume (in cu ft)
W_V = volume unit weight (lb/cu ft)

Building construction usually requires significant quantities of electrical conduit. Bundles of conduit are often lifted by cranes to the upper floors of multistory buildings.

Common Material Densities	
Material	**Weight***
Steel	490
Aluminum	165
Concrete	150
Wood	50
Water	62
Sand and gravel	120
Copper	560
Oil	58

* in lb/cuft

Figure 1-3. The density of a material is used to calculate the weight of an object with a known volume.

For example, what is the weight of a steel billet (block) measuring 1′ wide by 6″ high by 10′ long? The volume of the billet is 5 cu ft (1′ × 0.5′ × 10′ = 5 cu ft). *Note:* The density of this steel is 490 lb/cu ft.

$$W_{total} = V \times W_V$$
$$W_{total} = 5 \times 490$$
$$W_{total} = \textbf{2450 lb}$$

Determining the total surface area or volume of a complex object may involve breaking it down into simpler shapes (triangles, cubes, circles, etc.), finding their individual surface area or volume, and adding them back together to determine the total amount. **See Figure 1-4.**

For example, the total surface area of a cylindrical tank made from steel plate can be determined by adding the calculated circular base and top areas to the rectangular side. **See Figure 1-5.** The tank is 5′ in diameter, 8′ high, and made from ¼″ thick steel (weighing 10.2 lb/sq ft). What is the total weight of the tank?

> ⚡ **Factoid**
>
> Rounding up of dimensions or calculations simplifies calculations and either accounts for additional small components or adds an extra margin of safety, especially when rounding beyond the customary rules.

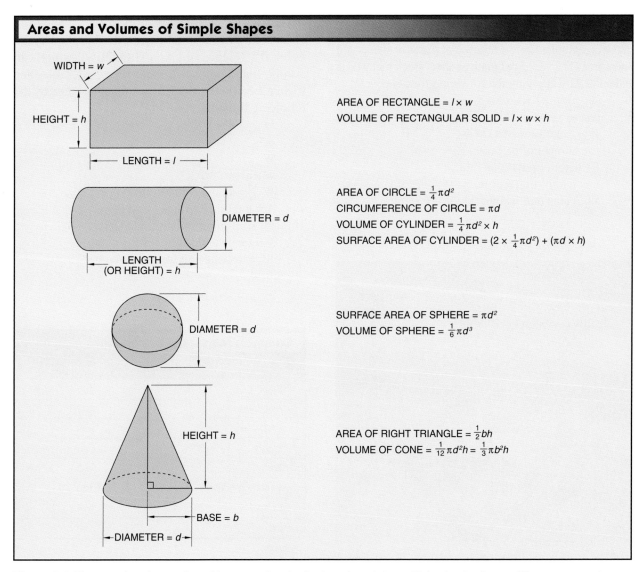

Areas and Volumes of Simple Shapes

WIDTH = w
HEIGHT = h
LENGTH = l

AREA OF RECTANGLE = $l \times w$
VOLUME OF RECTANGULAR SOLID = $l \times w \times h$

DIAMETER = d
LENGTH (OR HEIGHT) = h

AREA OF CIRCLE = $\frac{1}{4}\pi d^2$
CIRCUMFERENCE OF CIRCLE = πd
VOLUME OF CYLINDER = $\frac{1}{4}\pi d^2 \times h$
SURFACE AREA OF CYLINDER = $(2 \times \frac{1}{4}\pi d^2) + (\pi d \times h)$

DIAMETER = d

SURFACE AREA OF SPHERE = πd^2
VOLUME OF SPHERE = $\frac{1}{6}\pi d^3$

HEIGHT = h
BASE = b
DIAMETER = d

AREA OF RIGHT TRIANGLE = $\frac{1}{2}bh$
VOLUME OF CONE = $\frac{1}{12}\pi d^2 h = \frac{1}{3}\pi b^2 h$

Figure 1-4. The complex shape of an object can often be broken down into multiple simple shapes. The areas or volumes of these individual shapes are then added together to determine the total area or volume of the complex shape.

Tank Example

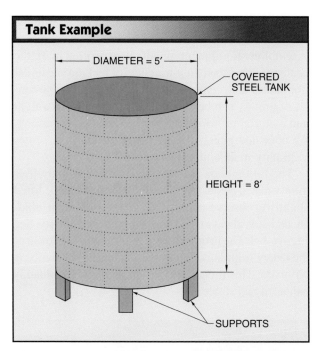

DIAMETER = 5′

COVERED STEEL TANK

HEIGHT = 8′

SUPPORTS

Figure 1-5. The weight of a steel sheet metal tank can be calculated by determining the total surface area of the tank and multiplying by the area unit weight of the material.

The top and bottom of the tank are circles. The area of each circle is calculated using the following formula:

$$A_{cir} = \frac{1}{4}\pi d^2$$

where

A_{cir} = area of circle (in sq ft)

π = 3.14

d = diameter (in ft)

$$A_{cir} = \frac{1}{4}\pi d^2$$

$$A_{cir} = \frac{1}{4} \times 3.14 \times 5^2$$

$$A_{cir} = 0.785 \times 25$$

$$A_{cir} = \textbf{19.6 sq ft}$$

The side of the tank is a rectangle, and the length is equal to the circumference of the circular base. The area is calculated with the following formula:

$$A_{cyl} = \pi d \times h$$

where

A_{cyl} = area of cylinder side (in sq ft)

π = 3.14

d = diameter (in ft)

h = height (in ft)

$$A_{cyl} = \pi d \times h$$

$$A_{cyl} = 3.14 \times 5 \times 8$$

$$A_{cyl} = \textbf{126 sq ft}$$

The total area of the tank is 165.2 sq ft (19.6 + 19.6 + 126 = 165.2 sq ft). The total weight of the tank is then determined by multiplying the total area by the area unit weight.

$$W_{total} = A \times W_A$$

$$W_{total} = 165.2 \times 10.2$$

$$W_{total} = \textbf{1685 lb}$$

This calculation excludes any additional components that add weight to the tank, such as fasteners, supports, pipe flanges, or valves. Therefore, if a load includes additional small components, their weight is usually estimated and added to the total. In the case of the tank, the total load weight is estimated at 1800 lb. Alternatively, the measured dimensions can all be rounded up slightly before calculating areas or volumes, which makes calculations faster and either accounts for additional components or increases the margin of safety.

Load Balance

Loads must be lifted in a controlled manner. Any shifting, tipping, or rocking of the load may cause the rigging to fail, allowing the load to fall, be damaged, and/or injure a worker. The rigging must be arranged so that the load remains stable and level when lifted. This requires determining the load's center of gravity. **See Figure 1-6.**

Load Balance

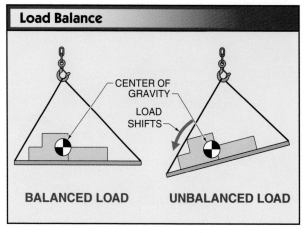

CENTER OF GRAVITY

LOAD SHIFTS

BALANCED LOAD   **UNBALANCED LOAD**

Figure 1-6. A load must be lifted from directly over the center of gravity in order to maintain balance.

Center of Gravity. The *center of gravity* is the balancing point of a load. The center of gravity, also known as the center of mass in this context, is the point at which an object's total mass can be considered to be concentrated. All of the load's weight is considered to be located at this single point for all calculations and comparisons. Lifting a load from directly over its center of gravity puts the least stress on the rigging and provides the safest and most controllable lifting conditions.

The distribution of mass in a load determines its center of gravity. **See Figure 1-7.** A *symmetrical load* is a load in which one half of the load is a mirror image of the other half. Symmetrical loads are typically visually symmetrical between their two sides. The center of gravity of a symmetrical load is at or very near its physical center. Symmetrical loads include straight pipes, motors, paper rolls, and sheet metal. An *asymmetrical load* is a load in which one half of the load is substantially different from the other half. Asymmetrical loads include most machinery, motor and pump assemblies, pipe and valve assemblies, and engines. The center of gravity of an asymmetrical load is likely not at its physical center.

The center of gravity of a load must be determined before lifting, though this can be difficult with complex assemblies. Equipment manufacturers often mark the center of gravity on their products or include specification sheets with center of gravity information. The center of gravity can be calculated precisely from weight and material information, but this is time-consuming. An educated guess may be made, placing the center of gravity in an approximate location.

The lifting hook should be positioned directly over the estimated center of gravity. The load should be lifted slightly to observe stability and weight shifting. Unbalanced loads always tilt toward the center of gravity. **See Figure 1-8.** The lifting equipment is readjusted towards the heavy (dipping) side of the load if an imbalance is observed. This procedure is continued until the load is balanced and stable.

> ⚡ **Factoid**
>
> The term "center of gravity" is often considered to be synonymous with "center of mass." However, the latter term is broader and covers any circumstance. In the context of rigging and lifting, with constant and uniform gravity, "center of gravity" is an appropriate usage.

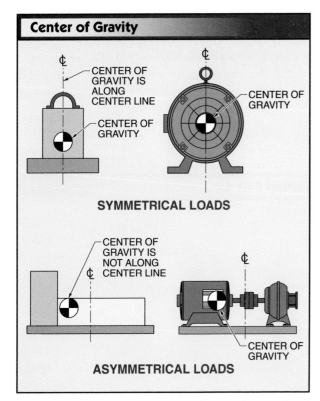

Figure 1-7. The symmetry of a load is sometimes a visual clue to the location of the center of gravity.

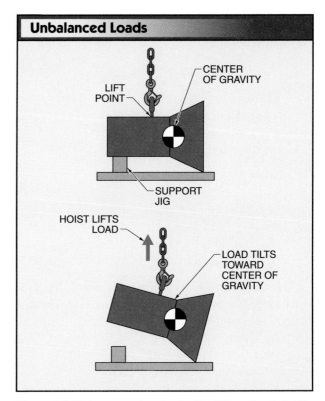

Figure 1-8. Balance can be checked by lifting a load slightly and checking to see if it is level.

It is also critical to consider the vertical position of the center of gravity point. Lifting from below this point (through rigging attachments) makes the load less stable. Slight wobbling during the lift, due to the motion of the hoist, can cause the load to topple. **See Figure 1-9.** If the load must be lifted from points below the center of gravity, stability is improved somewhat by rigging the lift hook well above the center of gravity.

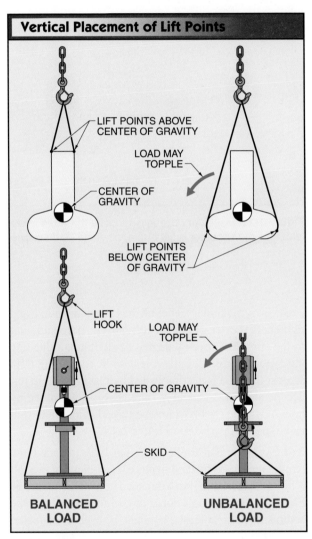

Figure 1-9. The vertical location of the lift points in relation to the center of gravity also affects the stability of a load.

Lift Points. If a load cannot be lifted from only one point directly over the center of gravity, multiple lift points are needed. A single hoist may still be used, but a rigging arrangement is needed to distribute the lifting forces to multiple points. This can greatly improve the balance and control of the load, but only

if the lift points are placed correctly. Lift points may involve hardware already installed in the load by the manufacturer or may require the rigger to determine their placement.

If a load is lifted from two points spaced equally from the center of gravity, then each supports half of the load weight. **See Figure 1-10.** However, if one point is closer to the center of gravity than the other, it supports a greater share of the load. The share is proportional to the relative distance of the other lift point from the center of gravity. This unequal loading causes excessive stress on the rigging components and may create an unsafe lifting situation.

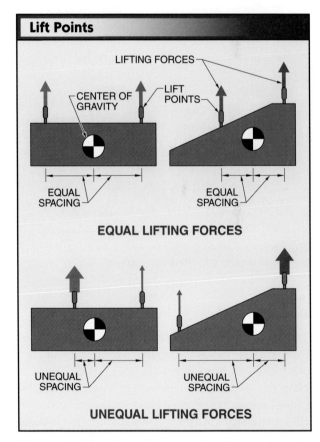

Figure 1-10. The relative distances of the lift points from the center of gravity determine their share of the load weight.

EYEBOLTS

Some loads are preequipped by the manufacturer with lifting lugs or eyebolts as lift points, which simplifies balancing, rigging, and lifting. A *lifting lug* is a thick metal loop welded or fastened to a load to provide a lift point.

An *eyebolt* is a bolt with a looped head that is fastened to a load to provide a lift point. **See Figure 1-11.** Eyebolts are attached by screwing them into a threaded hole or inserting an eyebolt shank through a hole and securing the eyebolt with a nut.

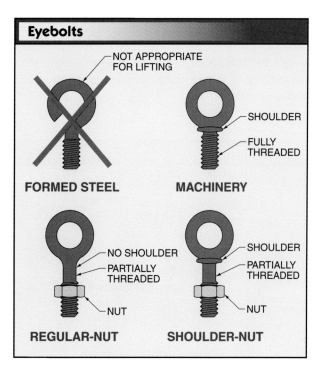

Figure 1-11. Forged machinery or nut eyebolts are used in various rigging and lifting applications.

Eyebolt Types

The loop of an eyebolt may be formed or forged. Formed loops are rods that are bent around to form a loop. Because one end is open and the steel was deformed to make the loop, these loops are not strong enough for lifting applications. Forged loops are pressed into their closed-loop shape in a process that keeps the steel strong. Only forged steel eyebolts should be used for lifting applications. Three common types of forged eyebolts are machinery, regular-nut, and shoulder-nut eyebolts.

Machinery Eyebolts. The machinery eyebolt is the most commonly used eyebolt. Machinery eyebolts are fully threaded and must be screwed in until the shoulder is tight against the load. **See Figure 1-12.** Washers must be used to create a tight shoulder-to-load fit if the shoulder is not sharp and the load surface has not been countersunk.

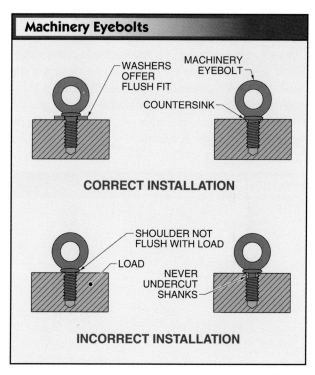

Figure 1-12. Machinery eyebolts must be threaded into a load until the shoulder is tight up against the load surface.

After a machinery eyebolt has been installed and tightened, the eye of the eyebolt must be perpendicular to the sling line for any degree of side pull. Adjusting the eyebolt for proper alignment while remaining tight against the load is accomplished by placing a shim under the shoulder. The shim thickness is determined by how much the eyebolt must be turned (unthreaded) to be aligned properly. **See Figure 1-13.**

Nut Eyebolts. Nut eyebolts are not fully threaded and require nuts to be secured in place. A regular-nut eyebolt is normally screwed into a threaded hole in the load. **See Figure 1-14.** If the hole does not go through the load, the depth should be at least 2½ times the eyebolt diameter, and the eyebolt should be screwed into the load to a minimum depth of 2 times the eyebolt diameter. A nut on the loop side of the eyebolt ensures that the eyebolt is tight.

One or more nuts are also used when the hole passes completely through the load. For a threaded hole in thick (greater than one eyebolt diameter) material, a nut secures the attachment from the bolt end. For thinner materials, a nut is required in both sides. For an unthreaded hole, two nuts are firmly tightened against each other on the bolt end with a third nut on the loop side.

Alignment for Angular Forces

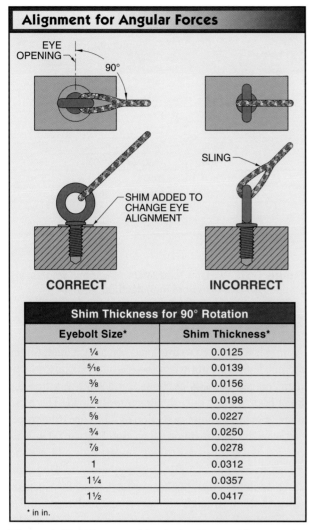

Shim Thickness for 90° Rotation	
Eyebolt Size*	Shim Thickness*
1/4	0.0125
5/16	0.0139
3/8	0.0156
1/2	0.0198
5/8	0.0227
3/4	0.0250
7/8	0.0278
1	0.0312
1 1/4	0.0357
1 1/2	0.0417

* in in.

Figure 1-13. When used in rigging that applies angular forces, eyebolts must be turned until the loop is in line with the rigging.

When a shoulder-nut eyebolt is used, the threaded portion of the shank must protrude through the load sufficiently to allow full engagement of the nut. **See Figure 1-15.** A fully engaged nut has no portion of internal thread not in contact with the bolt. Washers are used if the unthreaded portion of the shoulder nut eyebolt protrudes so far that the nut cannot be tightened securely against the load.

Angular forces should only be applied to an eyebolt that is firmly supported against the load surface by a shoulder. Therefore, a regular-nut eyebolt and a shoulder-nut eyebolt (where the shoulder is not used) should never be used with rigging that pulls on eyebolts at an angle.

Shoulder-Nut Eyebolts

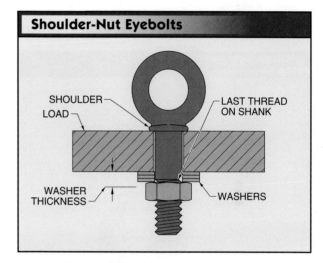

Figure 1-15. Shoulder-nut eyebolts have a shoulder that can be placed tight up against the load surface but require a nut to secure the opposite end.

Regular-Nut Eyebolts

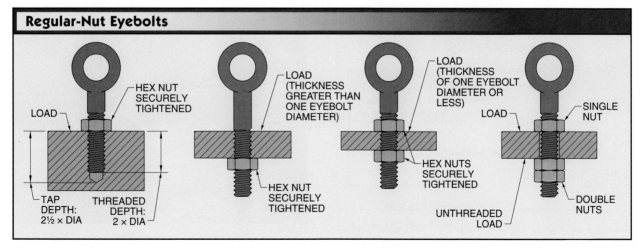

Figure 1-14. Regular-nut eyebolts use one to three nuts to secure the eyebolt against the load.

Eyebolt Load Capacity

The load capacity of an eyebolt is greatest when it is pulled vertically in a direction directly opposite to the shank. When forces are angular, the effective capacity of the eyebolt is reduced. **See Figure 1-16.** Specific load rating information must be obtained for a particular eyebolt because actual eyebolt load ratings vary significantly between manufacturers. However, general lifting capacities of eyebolts may be used as a primary estimation when designing lifting assemblies. **See Figure 1-17.**

➕ Safety Tip

If it may be loaded from the side, an eyebolt must be oriented correctly and have a shoulder that is seated firmly against the load. The shoulder is a critical part of the eyebolt's resistance to angular forces.

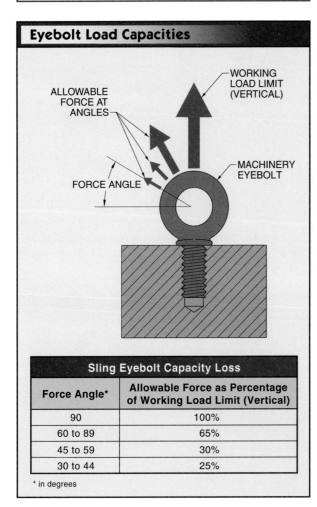

Eyebolt Load Capacities

Sling Eyebolt Capacity Loss	
Force Angle*	Allowable Force as Percentage of Working Load Limit (Vertical)
90	100%
60 to 89	65%
45 to 59	30%
30 to 44	25%

* in degrees

Figure 1-16. Eyebolts have the greatest load capacity when used with vertical forces. The capacity at other angles is a percentage of the vertical working load limit.

Shouldered Eyebolts Working Load Limits

Eyebolt Size*	Working Load Limit at Force Angle†			
	90°	60°	45°	30°
¼	650	420	195	160
⁵⁄₁₆	1200	780	360	300
⅜	1550	1000	465	380
½	2600	1690	780	650
⅝	5200	3380	1560	1300
¾	7200	4680	2160	1800
⅞	10,600	6890	3180	2650
1	13,300	8645	3990	3325
1¼	21,000	13,650	6300	5250
1½	24,000	15,600	7200	6000

* in in.
† in lb

Figure 1-17. Working load limits at various angles are sometimes available from manufacturer tables.

SLINGS

A *sling* is a line used to lift, lower, or carry a load. Slings are needed for lifting when there are no existing attachment points, such as eyebolts, on a load or when the hoist hook cannot directly attach to the load. The main component of a sling is a section of wire rope, fiber rope, chain, webbing, or round sling. **See Figure 1-18.** This portion is often used to wrap underneath and around a load to hold it securely. Rigging hardware used with slings includes clips, hooks, eyebolts, shackles, sockets, wedge sockets, triangle choker fittings, and master links. **See Figure 1-19.**

Lift-All Company, Inc.
Slings are available in a variety of materials, sizes, hardware attachments, and capacity ratings.

Slings

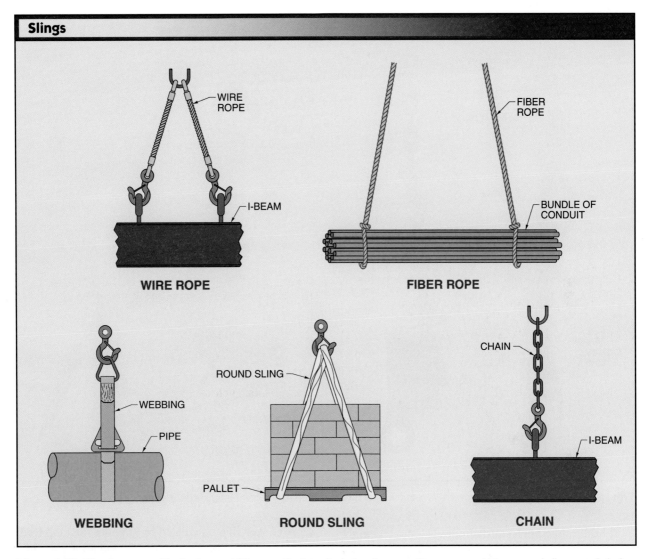

Figure 1-18. Sling types used in rigging and lifting applications include wire rope, fiber rope, webbing, round slings, and chain.

Sling Hitches

A *sling hitch* is a sling arrangement that has a loop at both ends to rig a load for lifting. Basic sling hitches include the vertical, bridle, basket, and choker arrangements. **See Figure 1-20.** The type of sling hitch affects the available lifting capacity for two reasons: the number of slings determines the portion of load each carries, and the angle of the sling determines its resulting force.

A vertical sling hitch is the simplest hitch and basically an extension of the hoisting line. Lifting with a vertical sling creates a straight, vertical pull. A single-leg vertical sling hitch is used to lift loads such as pumps, motors, gear drives, or any device equipped with a single eyebolt or lifting lug.

When using multiple slings in a rigging arrangement, all slings should have the same amount of stretch to avoid overloading individual legs and unbalancing the load during the lift.

Rigging Hardware

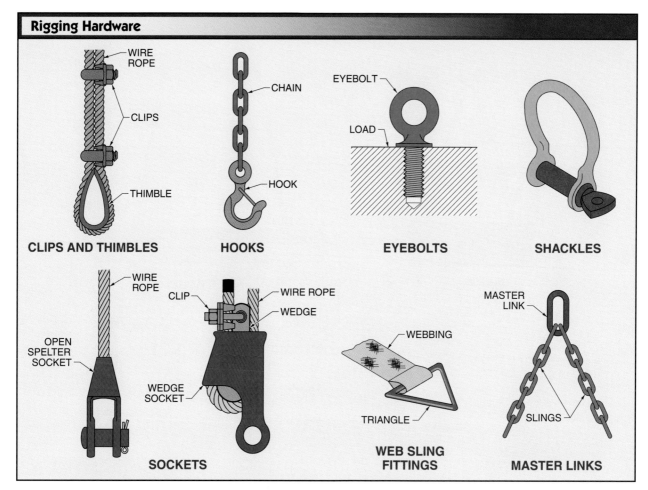

CLIPS AND THIMBLES — WIRE ROPE, CLIPS, THIMBLE

HOOKS — CHAIN, HOOK

EYEBOLTS — EYEBOLT, LOAD

SHACKLES

SOCKETS — WIRE ROPE, OPEN SPELTER SOCKET, CLIP, WIRE ROPE, WEDGE, WEDGE SOCKET

WEB SLING FITTINGS — WEBBING, TRIANGLE

MASTER LINKS — MASTER LINK, SLINGS

Figure 1-19. Various rigging hardware is used with slings to attach slings to hoists, loads, and other slings.

A bridle sling hitch consists of two or more straight slings (of the same type) that bring multiple lifting points on the load to a single hoisting point. Bridle sling hitches are typically used for large or complex shaped loads, such as machinery or long lengths of material. The use of multiple slings divides the load weight, increases load stability, and allows the rigging to be arranged so that the hoist is directly over the center of gravity. The disadvantage is that because the slings are at an angle, they experience greater forces.

A basket sling hitch uses one sling that is looped under the load so that both ends can be connected to the hoist. The two eye loops may be attached to the hoist at a single hook, which is similar to a bridle hitch, or to two separate hooks. If the ends of the sling are attached to different hooks of the hoist so that they lift vertically, the hoist may be called a U-sling hoist. If the sling ends are at an angle, they are subject to increased forces.

A choker sling is created by slipping the loop from one end of the sling over the other end after wrapping the load. The point above the load at which the choker sling meets is the choke junction. Choker slings are commonly used with loads such as pipes, bars, or poles that are drawn together in a bundle. Slings in choker hitches also experience greater forces due to the angle of pull at the choke junction.

Angular Sling Load Forces

The slings in bridle, basket, and choker sling hitches work at an angle, which increases the forces they experience beyond their portion of the load weight. **See Figure 1-21.** The *sling angle* is the angle between the horizontal and the sling. The sling angle decreases as the width between the lift points increases. The weight of the load is combined with the reaction forces holding the lift points apart. Smaller sling angles result in greater sling forces. Due to the extreme forces involved, sling angles less than 30° are not recommended.

Basic Sling Combinations

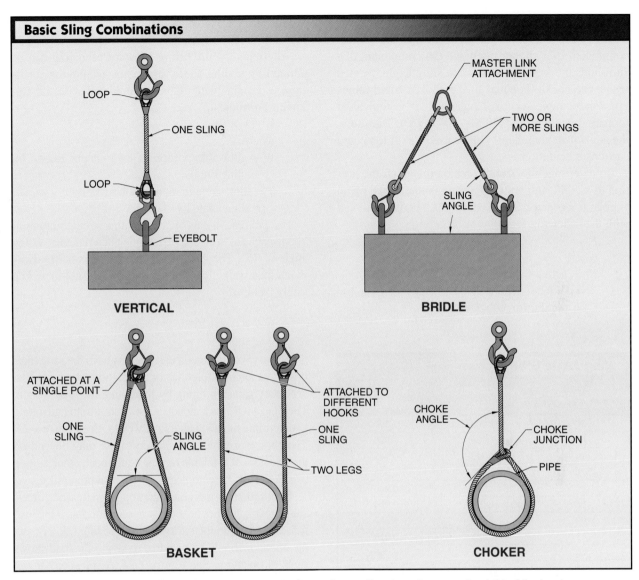

Figure 1-20. Slings are used in various arrangements depending on the size, shape, and weight of the load.

Sling Angles

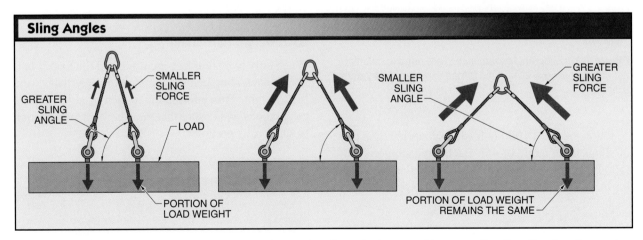

Figure 1-21. When multiple slings are used, the sling angle affects the increased forces on the sling. Smaller sling angles result in greater sling forces.

Choker hitches form a choke angle at the choke junction. The *choke angle* is the angle between the vertical component of a choker hitch and the component that surrounds the load. An equivalent sling angle, formed inside the choke, is equal to the choker angle minus 90°. For example, a choker angle of 135° is equivalent to a sling angle of 45° (135° − 90° = 45°). Therefore, the equivalent sling angle can be used for all force and capacity calculations.

To determine the actual force on the sling, the portion of weight supported by a sling is multiplied by an angular force factor. **See Figure 1-22.** This is calculated with the following formula:

$$F_{act} = W \times f_{AF}$$

where

F_{act} = actual force on sling (in lb)

W = portion of load weight carried by sling (in lb)

f_{AF} = angular force factor

Sling Angle Load Factors

Sling Angle*	Angular Force Factor	Sling Angle Loss Factor
90	1.000	1.000
85	1.004	0.996
80	1.015	0.985
75	1.035	0.966
70	1.064	0.940
65	1.103	0.906
60	1.155	0.866
55	1.221	0.819
50	1.305	0.766
45	1.414	0.707
40	1.556	0.643
35	1.743	0.574
30	2.000	0.500

* in degrees

Figure 1-22. Sling angle load factors are used to calculate the affect of sling angle on the forces experienced by each sling.

For example, a 1000 lb load is supported by a pair of slings at an angle of 45°. Each sling supports half (500 lb) of the load and at 45°, the angular force factor is 1.414. What is the actual force experienced by each sling?

$$F_{act} = W \times f_{AF}$$
$$F_{act} = 500 \times 1.414$$
$$F_{act} = \textbf{707 lb}$$

Therefore, the strength rating of each sling must be at least 707 lb (not including safety factors), not just 500 lb.

Alternatively, the lifting capacity of a sling can be derated by a sling angle loss factor accounting for its rigging arrangement. This is calculated with the following formula:

$$W = S_r \times f_{SA}$$

where

W = allowable portion of load weight carried by sling (in lb)

S_r = sling strength rating (in lb)

f_{SA} = sling angle loss factor

For example, a pair of slings with a strength rating of 700 lb each are to be used in a bridle hitch rigged at a sling angle of 45°. The sling angle loss factor is 0.707. How much load weight can each sling support (not including safety factors)?

$$W = S_r \times f_{SA}$$
$$W = 700 \times 0.707$$
$$W = \textbf{500 lb}$$

These two sling angle calculations have the same purpose. The angular force factor calculation determines the necessary capacity rating by increasing the load weight. The sling angle loss factor decreases a sling's strength rating to determine the allowable load weight. **See Figure 1-23.** The choice of which calculation to use may depend on the selection of available rigging equipment, other rigging calculations to be completed, or personal preference.

In addition to the consideration of increased forces, angular sling hitches are not always appropriate if the load is flexible. If in doubt, the load should be lifted slowly, and the operator should be prepared to stop if the load shows signs of buckling. **See Figure 1-24.** A spreader bar can be used to change the direction of the forces to vertical in order to stabilize the load.

Load Weight Portioning

When only two sling legs are used, and the load is balanced, each sling can be assumed to carry half of the load weight. This information is then used to perform calculations and ensure that the sling is strong enough to support its portion.

⚡ **Factoid**

A choker hitch forms the equivalent of a basket hitch that joins at a point close to the load. In order to maximize the sling angle and minimize the forces on the slings, the choke junction should not be pushed down close to the load.

Angular Sling Load Force Calculations

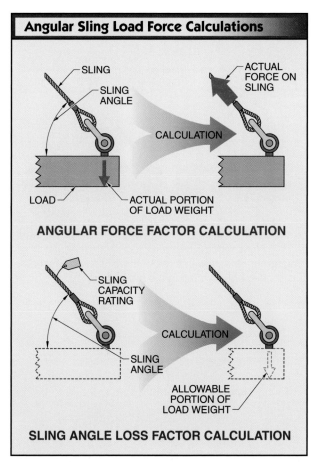

ANGULAR FORCE FACTOR CALCULATION

SLING ANGLE LOSS FACTOR CALCULATION

Figure 1-23. The angular force factor calculates the actual sling forces, which must be less than the sling capacity. The sling angle loss factor calculates a derated sling capacity due to sling angle, which must be greater than the portion of load weight supported by the sling. Either calculation accomplishes the same result.

Rigging can also be arranged with three or more sling legs. However, with more than two legs, an equal distribution of load weight across the slings becomes increasingly more difficult to ensure. Therefore, it is assumed that at least one of the legs carries no weight and provides stability only. **See Figure 1-25.** This adds a greater margin of safety that accounts for the likely unequal loading of the sling legs.

Each leg of a rigging arrangement with three legs is assumed to carry half of the load weight, and each leg of a rigging arrangement with four or more legs is assumed to carry one-third of the load weight. These load weight portions are then used to calculate actual forces on angular slings (if applicable) and ensure that the sling strength is adequate.

Spreader Bars

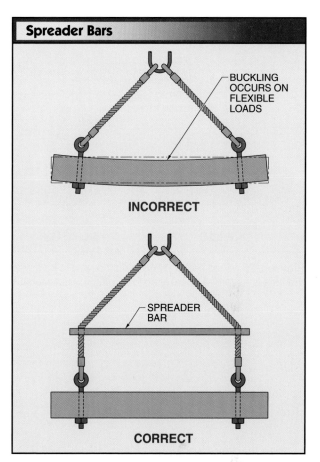

INCORRECT

CORRECT

Figure 1-24. If angular forces cause a flexible load to buckle, a spreader bar can be added to the rigging to change the direction of the forces on the load.

Lift-All Company, Inc.
A spreader bar is used to change the sling angle of certain slings in order to avoid buckling or interference from other components.

Load Weight Portioning

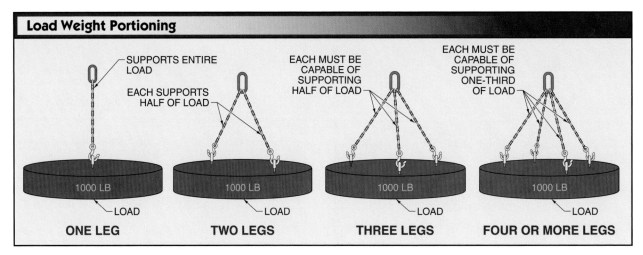

Figure 1-25. When calculating the distribution of load weight in sling arrangements with three or more legs, at least one of the legs is assumed to carry no load weight. As a result, the load is divided equally among the others legs.

Rope 2

The history of rope spans at least ten thousand years and yet it is still a critical part of most rigging and lifting applications. Although new materials have improved the strength, flexibility, durability, and other desirable characteristics of various ropes, the basic method of construction remains the same. The twisting and grouping together of various filaments produces a continuous line that is useful in various ways. Rope can be used to bind loads together, build rigging, and lift loads. Wire ropes have high strength and are particularly suitable as the lifting line in cranes. Fiber ropes have high flexibility and are particularly suitable for use with pulleys.

Objectives

- Describe the construction of ropes and the related terminology.
- Evaluate the safe load limit for ropes based on the appropriate safety factor.
- Compare the effects of bends on the effective strength of ropes.
- Detail the procedures for seizing or whipping rope.
- Describe the specific construction, characteristics, and applications of wire rope.
- Describe the specific construction, characteristics, and applications of fiber rope.

ROPE CONSTRUCTION

Rope is a length of fibers or thin wires that are twisted or braided together to form a strong and flexible line. **See Figure 2-1.** Rope is manufactured from metal wire, natural fibers, or synthetic fibers. Fiber rope is constructed by twisting fibers into yarn, yarn into strands, and strands into rope. *Yarn* is a continuous line of fibers twisted together. A *strand* is several pieces of yarn or wire twisted spirally around an axis. Multiple strands are then twisted to form the rope. Wire rope is constructed by twisting wires into strands and strands into wire rope.

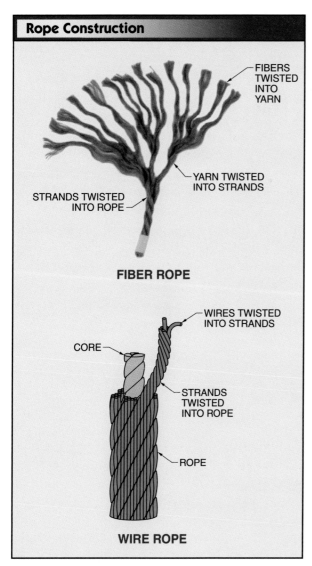

Figure 2-1. Rope is constructed from fibers, yarn or wire, and strands. These components are twisted together in various ways to form strong and flexible rope.

Rope Lay

The *lay* is a designation for the direction in which the strands are twisted, specified as they spiral away from the observer. **See Figure 2-2.** *Right-lay rope* is rope with strands that spiral to the right (clockwise). *Left-lay rope* is rope with strands that spiral to the left (counterclockwise). The lay of the strands, in combination with the twist direction of the yarn or wires, results in regular-lay or lang-lay rope.

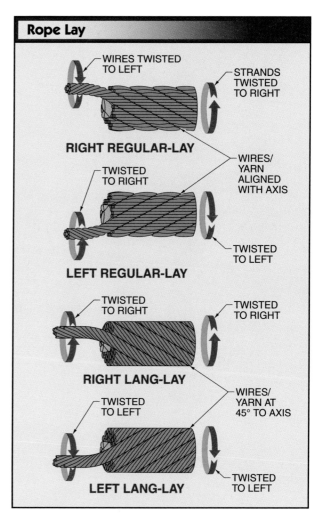

Figure 2-2. The directions of the strand and rope twist affect some of the characteristics of rope, such as flexibility, wear, and tendency to rotate.

A *regular-lay rope* is a rope in which the yarn or wires in the strands are twisted in the opposite direction of the lay of the strands. In a right regular-lay rope, the strands are laid to the right, and the yarn or wires are laid to the left. Similarly, in a left regular-lay rope, the strands are laid to the left, and the yarn or wires are laid to the right. Regular-lay rope is easily identified because the yarn or wires follow the direction of the axis of the rope. Right regular-lay rope resists untwisting under load.

A *lang-lay rope* is a rope in which the yarn or wires and strands are laid in the same direction. A right lang-lay rope has yarn or wires that are laid to the right and strands that are laid to the right. A left lang-lay rope has yarn or wires that are laid to the left and strands that are laid to the left. Lang-lay ropes are quickly identified by their yarn or wires crossing the axis of the rope at approximately 45°. Lang-lay ropes expose more of the yarn or wires to wear at the outer surface, which increases the useful life. Lang-lay ropes also have greater flexibility, but have a tendency to untwist under tension.

Since it is constructed from twisted strands, rope may spin or rotate when used. *Cabling* is a rope's tendency to rotate and untwist when under load. This must not be allowed because it transfers all the load weight to the shorter, center core. Rotation-resistant ropes that consist of two or more layers of strand laid in opposing directions are available to counteract the cabling tendency. These ropes require special handling because they are susceptible to kinking, crushing, and unbalancing. They also tend to have lower breaking strengths than similarly sized ropes.

> **⚡ Factoid**
>
> To some degree, rope strength varies according to the degree of twist in each construction step. A high-strength rope has less twist, which is referred to as "soft lay." Rope with a high resistance to abrasion has more twist, which is referred to as "hard lay."

Rope Diameter

The diameter of wire rope is the smallest possible dimension that fully encircles the rope. **See Figure 2-3.** The rope is measured from a high spot on one side of the rope to the high spot on the opposite side using calipers. Normally, new ropes are slightly larger in diameter than the specifications indicate.

Fiber rope can stretch under tension, which slightly reduces its diameter. Also, because it is relatively soft and flexible, it is difficult to measure the diameter precisely. Therefore, fiber rope diameters are given in nominal sizes or close approximations of the average size. A *nominal value* is a designated value that may vary slightly from the actual value.

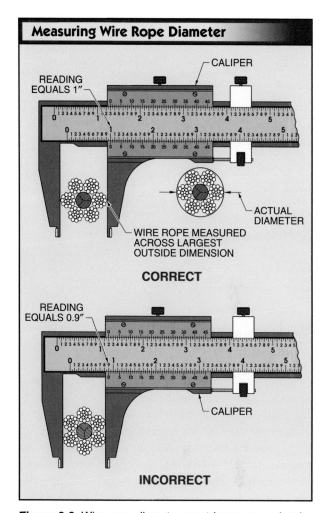

Figure 2-3. Wire rope diameter must be measured at its widest point.

Rope Strength

The breaking strength of rope is specified based on new rope, though only a portion of that strength may be used for lifting. A rope loses strength during use due to bending, exposure to moisture, extreme temperature, and chemical activity. Rope wear that reduces strength is indicated by abrasion marks, stretching or breaking of wire or fibers, or a reduction in rope diameter.

Working Load Limits. The strength rating of rope is its breaking strength. **See Figure 2-4.** The breaking strength of rope is obtained from tests where samples of rope are tensioned under increasing loads until they break. Many samples are tested and the results provide an average breaking strength for a particular type and size of rope.

Breaking Strengths of Selected Wire Ropes*

Diameter†	Improved Plow Steel		Extra-Improved Plow Steel
	Fiber Core	IWRC‡	IWRC‡
1/4	5340	5740	6640
5/16	8300	8940	10,280
3/8	11,900	12,800	14,720
7/16	16,120	17,340	19,900
1/2	20,800	22,400	26,000
9/16	26,400	28,200	32,800
5/8	32,600	35,000	40,200
3/4	46,400	50,000	57,400
7/8	62,800	67,400	77,600
1	81,600	87,600	100,800

* in lb, for uncoated, general purpose, rotation-resistant 6 × 19 (class 2) or 6 × 37 (class 3) wire rope

† in in.

‡ independent wire rope core

Figure 2-4. The breaking strengths of wire ropes vary by type, material, and size.

However, the breaking strength value cannot be used directly as a working load limit for lifting. The *working load limit* is the maximum weight that a rigging component may be subjected to. Loading a rope up to its breaking strength offers no margin of safety for underestimated load weight, rope age, or other weakening conditions. Plus, slight manufacturing differences between the loaded rope and the actual tested samples mean that the working rope may break under slightly less load. Therefore, safe working load limits are established by dividing the breaking strength by a safety factor. **See Figure 2-5.** A *safety factor* is the ratio of a component's ultimate strength to its maximum allowable safe working load limit.

Safety factors in rigging and lifting are normally between 5 and 8. Therefore, the breaking strength is 5 to 8 times greater than the allowable safe load limit. For example, if a safety factor of 5 is used for a rigging assembly with a breaking strength of 5000 lb, the working load limit of the rigging assembly is 1000 lb (5000 lb ÷ 5 = 1000 lb). A safety factor of 5 is used for steady or even loads. A safety factor of 8 is used for uneven loads or lifts that may shock the slings.

The nominal breaking strength of rope is often rated in tons. One ton equals 2000 lb. Rope strength or load weight may need to be converted between pounds and tons during calculations, depending on the available information. Either unit may be used, as long as it is the only weight unit used in the calculation.

Safe Load Limits

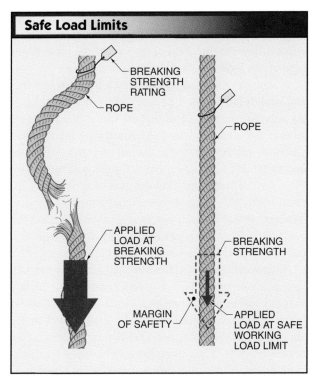

Figure 2-5. Rope must not be loaded beyond its safe working load limit, which is a fraction of its breaking strength.

The rope breaking strength rating needed to safely lift a load is calculated with the following formula:

$$S_b = WLL \times SF$$

where

S_b = rope breaking strength (in lb)

WLL = working load limit (in lb)

SF = safety factor

For example, what is the rope breaking strength required to lift a 4000 lb milling machine with a single vertical sling? *Note:* A safety factor of 5 is used because the load is a steady lift without shock.

$$S_b = WLL \times SF$$
$$S_b = 4000 \times 5$$
$$S_b = \textbf{20,000 lb or 10 t}$$

According to reference tables of rope breaking strengths provided by manufacturers, an acceptable specification of wire rope for lifting the machine is 1/2″ improved plow steel, fiber-core rope.

Many factors must be considered when determining the necessary strength of rigging ropes. For example, the use of multiple slings divides the total load weight between the slings, which reduces the strength requirements. However, the use of other sling hitch arrangements, such as basket, bridle, or choker sling hitches, increases the forces on the sling due to sling angle. Also, bends and attachment hardware reduce a rope's efficiency, lowering its effective strength. After taking into account all these factors with additional calculations, the total force on the sling must not exceed the effective working load limit. **See Figure 2-6.**

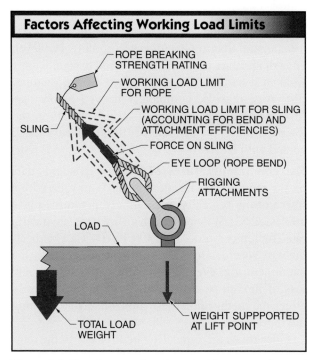

Figure 2-6. Many factors affect the actual force on a sling and the working load limit, which must not be exceeded.

Bending. Ropes are often wrapped over pulleys or around loads. This bending puts a rope under additional mechanical stress, which reduces its ability to withstand tension forces. **See Figure 2-7.** Bending a rope over a small diameter can reduce its effective strength by more than 50%. The *bending efficiency* is the ratio of the strength of a bent rope to its nominal strength rating. The *bend ratio* is the ratio of the diameter of a bend to the nominal diameter of the rope. The bend ratio is also known as the D/d ratio and is calculated with the following formula:

$$R_{bend} = \frac{D}{d}$$

where
R_{bend} = bend ratio
D = diameter of rope bend (in in.)
d = diameter of rope (in in.)

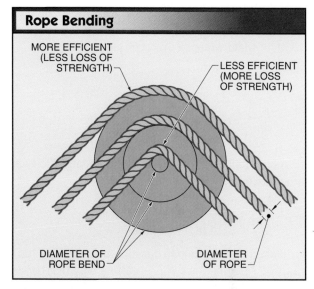

Figure 2-7. Tight bends reduce the effective strength of a rope and can permanently damage wires or fibers.

The calculated bend ratio is used to determine the rope bending efficiency according to a chart or plot. **See Figure 2-8.** This efficiency data is compiled by laboratories that conduct load tests on ropes. The efficiency percentage is then used with the rope's working load limit to calculate the resulting effective strength using the following formula:

$$S_{bend} = WLL \times \eta_{bend}$$

where
S_{bend} = rope bending strength (in lb)
WLL = rope working load limit (in lb)
η_{bend} = bending efficiency

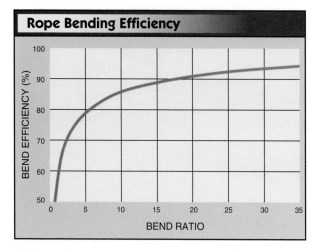

Figure 2-8. Rope bending efficiency increases with bend ratio.

For example, what is the rope bending strength of a ⅜″ (0.375″) rope, which has a working load limit of 1350 lb, when wrapped over a 6″ pulley?

$$R_{bend} = \frac{D}{d}$$

$$R_{bend} = \frac{6}{0.375}$$

$$R_{bend} = \mathbf{16}$$

A bend ratio of 16 corresponds to a bending efficiency of approximately 90%.

$$S_{bend} = S_{safe} \times \eta_{bend}$$
$$S_{bend} = 1350 \times 0.90$$
$$S_{bend} = \mathbf{1215\ lb}$$

Therefore, even though this rope has a working load limit of 1350 lb, since it is used in a way that bends the rope, it should not be subjected to forces greater than 1215 lb. This effective capacity can be increased by increasing the pulley diameter or using a different type of rope.

Bending efficiency can be increased when thimbles are used in rope ends or rope loops. A *thimble* is a curved piece of metal around which a rope is fitted to form a loop. The thimble increases the radius of the otherwise sharp bend and also protects the rope from abrasion.

Exposure to moisture or certain chemicals can corrode the metal of wire ropes.

Moisture Exposure. The effects of moisture vary between rope types. Moisture causes steel wire rope to rust, which is a type of corrosion. *Corrosion* is the disintegration of a material due to chemical reaction with its environment. Since the corrosion may occur on the inside first, a weakening due to rust may not be visible before the rope breaks. Wire ropes should be kept lubricated to prevent rusting.

Natural fibers can absorb moisture, which leads to decay or rot. Therefore, most rope manufacturers treat natural fiber rope with waterproofing. However, enough moisture may still be absorbed to significantly weaken a natural fiber rope when frozen. Natural fiber rope must be completely thawed before use. Most synthetic fibers do not absorb moisture, but the rope may still become brittle and weakened if coated with ice.

Extreme Temperatures. Manufacturers supply data on the temperature limits of rope. Wire rope with a fiber core is typically rated for temperatures up to 180°F (82°C). Wire rope with a wire core is typically rated for temperatures up to 400°F (204°C). Overheating wire rope destroys the lubrication applied during manufacturing, eventually leading to corrosion and loss of flexibility. Severe overheating may directly affect the metal properties, immediately weakening the rope.

Fiber ropes are typically rated for use in the temperature range of –20°F to 100°F (–29°C to 38°C). High temperatures dry out natural fibers, making them brittle and easily breakable. Synthetic fibers tend to soften in high temperatures, allowing the rope to stretch and lose strength. Very low temperatures tend to make either type of fiber brittle.

Chemical Activity. Exposure to corrosive chemicals can cause significant and rapid damage to rope. Rope used in chemically corrosive environments, such as battery shops, metal-plating shops, pickling plants, or pulp and paper mills, must be designed specifically to resist the chemicals present. Wire rope is made from stainless steel or coated with vinyl, nylon, Teflon®, or zinc for corrosion resistance. Natural fiber ropes cannot be used in these environments because they deteriorate immediately. Synthetic fibers withstand many chemical conditions, making synthetic fiber ropes particularly well suited for these uses. However, resistances vary, so the manufacturer's literature should always be consulted before using a rope in a chemical environment.

Seizing and Whipping

A rope end must be bound to prevent strand raveling or unsafe loose wires before cutting. Similar bindings are made for wire and fiber ropes, though they often go by different terms. *Seizing* is the wire wrapping that binds the end of a wire rope near where it is cut. **See Figure 2-9.** *Whipping* is the twine wrapping that binds the end of a fiber rope near where it is cut. The length of each seizing/whipping should be equal to or greater than the rope diameter. The binding holds the strands firmly in place by the tight turning of seizing wire or whipping twine. Adequate binding prevents rope distortion, flattening, or strand loosening. Inadequate binding shortens rope life by allowing uneven distribution of the strand load during lifting.

Seizing or whipping must be done before the cut is made. Normally, one seizing/whipping on each side of the planned cut is sufficient for fiber rope and preformed wire rope. *Preformed rope* is wire rope in which the strands are permanently formed into a helical shape during fabrication. The wires in preformed ropes do not easily unravel when cut. Common wire ropes (those that are not preformed or are rotation-resistant) normally require a minimum of two seizings on each side of the cut, placed six rope diameters apart. Seizing/whipping requirements vary based on rope size. Always check the manufacturer's specifications for recommendations.

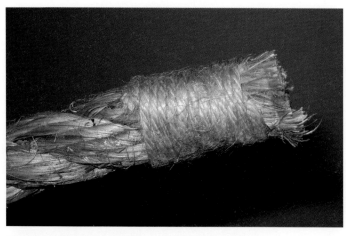

The ends of fiber rope are whipped to prevent unraveling.

The recommended method for seizing a wire rope is to lay one end of the seizing wire between two strands of the wire rope. The other end of the seizing wire is wrapped around the rope and the seizing wire. A seizing bar tool is placed at a right angle to the rope. The loose end of the seizing wire is brought around the back of the bar. The bar is then twisted around the rope to wind the seizing wire tightly around the rope, without overlapping, until the required seizing length is obtained. The seizing is secured by twisting the ends of the seizing wire together.

The wire rope is then cut using a rope shear, an abrasive cutoff wheel, or an oxyacetylene cutting torch. Shearing or abrasive cutting leaves a sharp edge that should be filed smooth. An oxyacetylene cutting torch is preferred because the heat also fuses the strands and strand wires together.

> **+ Safety Tip**
>
> Gloves should be worn when handling wire rope. Hands are easily cut by broken strand wires or the twisted ends of seizing wire.

Seizing Wire Rope

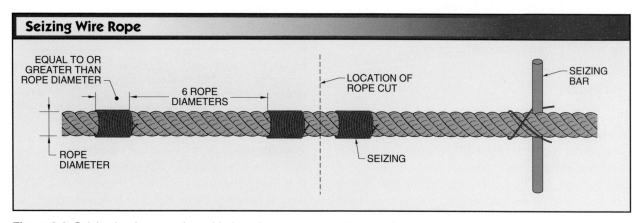

EQUAL TO OR GREATER THAN ROPE DIAMETER

6 ROPE DIAMETERS

LOCATION OF ROPE CUT

SEIZING BAR

ROPE DIAMETER

SEIZING

Figure 2-9. Seizing is wire wrapping added to wire rope to prevent unraveling or loose wires.

The end of a fiber rope is whipped with a similar procedure. **See Figure 2-10.** The whipping material is flexible twine or thin strands of synthetic fibers. The twine is formed into an elongated loop, which is laid along the rope to be whipped. The twine is wrapped tightly around the rope, gradually working toward the rope end. The turns are laid hard against each other without overlapping. When the whipping is of sufficient length, the loose end of the twine is tucked through the remaining loop. The loop is then drawn beneath the whipping by pulling the other end of the twine. Both loose ends of twine are trimmed, close to the turns, and the rope is ready to be cut. After cutting, the ends of some synthetic fiber ropes are also sealed with heat.

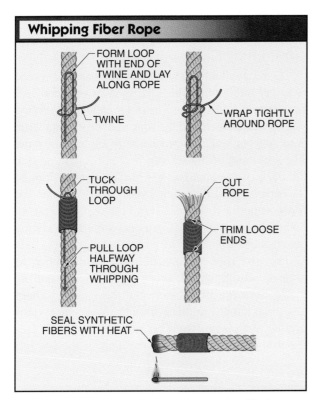

Figure 2-10. Fiber rope whipping is completed before cutting in order to bind all the strands together.

WIRE ROPE

Wire rope is a highly specialized precision product that is adaptable to many uses and conditions of operation. To meet the requirements of different types of service, ropes are designed and manufactured in a number of constructions and grades. The appropriate wire rope is selected based on the load weight, potential for shock from acceleration or deceleration, attachments needed, and lifting conditions.

Wire Metals

Rope wire can be made from several types of metal, including steel, iron, stainless steel, Monel®, and bronze. Wire rope manufacturers select the wire that is most appropriate for the requirements of the finished product. The most widely used material is steel with a high carbon content. This steel is available in a variety of grades, each providing slightly different properties to the steel rope wire. Grades of wire rope are traction steel (TS), mild plow steel (MPS), plow steel (PS), improved plow steel (IPS), and extra improved plow steel (EIPS).

Steel that is galvanized (coated with zinc) may be required for harsh or corrosive environments. Typical rigging and lifting wire rope is bright (uncoated). Galvanized wire rope is approximately 10% lower in strength than bright wire rope.

Wire Rope Construction

Wire rope is made of a specific number of strands wound spirally around a core. **See Figure 2-11.** Each strand is made of a number of metal wires. The strength and flexibility of a rope depends on the precise laying of each wire and the way they slide against each other as the rope flexes.

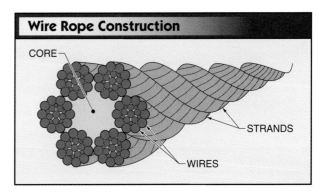

Figure 2-11. Wire rope is composed of a core surrounded by strands, each of which is composed of a specific pattern of wires of different sizes.

Wire Strand Patterns. Wire rope strands often use multiple sizes of wire, arranged in specific patterns, to provide desired flexibility and wear characteristics. While there are many patterns, the most common designs are filler wire, Warrington, Seale, and Warrington-Seale. **See Figure 2-12.**

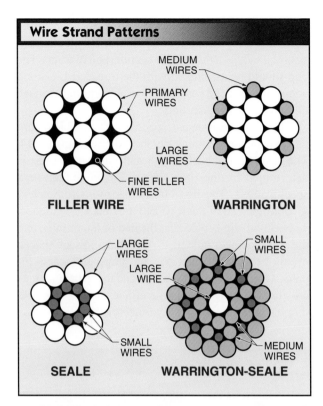

Wire Strand Patterns

MEDIUM
WIRES

PRIMARY
WIRES

LARGE
WIRES

FINE FILLER
WIRES

FILLER WIRE

WARRINGTON

LARGE
WIRES

SMALL
WIRES

LARGE
WIRE

SMALL
WIRES

MEDIUM
WIRES

SEALE

WARRINGTON-SEALE

Figure 2-12. The wires in strands can be arranged in different patterns, which changes the strength, flexibility, and wear characteristics.

Filler wire strands use fine wires to fill the gaps between the major wires. The fine wires provide stability to the shape of the strand but contribute little strength. Filler wire rope is the most flexible, but wears more than Warrington or Seale wire rope.

Warrington wire strands are constructed of two or more wire sizes. The Warrington pattern is easily distinguished by its alternating large and small wire sizes in the outer layer. The wire sizes in interior layers vary, depending on the strand size. Warrington wire rope is less flexible than filler wire rope, but has better wear resistance.

Seale wire strands also use multiple wire sizes, but not mixed within individual layers. All wires in the outermost layer are one size, and all wires in the next layer are another size. Seale wire rope is less flexible than Warrington wire rope but is the least susceptible to wear.

Combination Warrington-Seale wire strands compromise between wear and flexibility. The outer layer is typically a Seale pattern, used for better wear characteristics. An inner layer is a Warrington wire pattern

that provides increased flexibility. As strands are made with greater numbers of wire, various combination patterns are more common. Warrington and Seale patterns may be alternated for each layer, and filler wires may be added in between.

Wire Rope Cores. Wire rope strands are laid around a core. The core may be another wire strand, a small wire rope, or a strand made from a nonmetallic material, such as fiber or polyvinyl. A wire strand core (WSC) is a single strand constructed of multiple wires. This core strand is typically of the same size and pattern as the rope strands. An independent wire rope core (IWRC) is a small wire rope, often the 6 × 7 design made from smaller wires. Wire ropes with an IWRC resist crushing and have consistent stretching properties. A fiber core (FC) is made of sisal or manila fibers and is shaped to keep the strands in place and cushioned. Fiber cores contribute greater flexibility to wire rope, but are not as strong as WSC or IWRC types. Polyvinyl cores are used in wire rope intended for chemical resistance.

Wire Rope Designations. Wire rope is classified according to the number of strands in the rope and the number of wires in each strand. For example, a 6 × 19 rope indicates a six-stranded rope with approximately 19 wires per strand. The second number in the designation is nominal in that the number of wires in a strand may be slightly higher or lower. A 6 × 7 rope consists of six strands with 3 to 14 wires per strand. A 6 × 19 classification consists of six strands with 15 to 26 wires per strand. The 6 × 19 classification includes constructions such as 6 × 21 filler wire, 6 × 25 filler wire, and 6 × 26 Warrington-Seale. These constructions are all classified as 6 × 19 rope, despite the fact that none of their strands have exactly 19 wires.

Letter acronyms are added to rope designations to indicate the rope construction, wire material, core material, core construction, strand pattern, and other specifications. **See Figure 2-13.** For example, the designation "6 × 19W+FC RH OL FSWR" indicates a six-strand flexible steel wire rope with approximately 19 wires per strand in a Warrington pattern, fiber core, and right-hand ordinary (regular) lay.

> ⚡ **Factoid**
>
> Rope must be protected from abrasion or cutting when it is used with equipment or loads that have rough surfaces or sharp corners. Protection pads should be placed over any part of the load that will contact the rope during lifting.

Rope Designation Acronyms

Rope Construction

RH	Right-hand lay
LH	Left-hand lay
RL	Regular lay
OL	Ordinary (regular) lay
LL	Lang lay
AL	Alternate lay
RR	Rotation-resistant
NR	Nonrotating

Materials

TS	Traction steel
MPS	Mild plow steel
PS	Plow steel
IPS	Improved plow steel
GIPS	Galvanized improved plow steel
EIPS	Extra improved plow steel
FSWR	Flexible steel wire rope
J	Jute (fiber)

Strand Patterns

FW	Filler wire
S	Seale
SF	Seale filler wire
W	Warrington
SW	Seale-Warrington
WS	Warrington-Seale
TS	Triangular strand

Cores

FC	Fiber core
HC	Sisal core
WSC	Wire strand core
IWS	Independent wire strand
WRC	Wire rope core
IWR	Independent wire rope
IWRC	Independent wire rope core

Figure 2-13. Rope designations use letter acronyms to indicate various rope characteristics.

Wire Rope Terminations

Wire rope ends must be fastened to fittings or spliced into loops in order to attach the rope to a load. Fittings may not have the same strength as the rope, reducing the strength efficiency. Common wire rope terminations include thimbles and sockets.

Thimbles. A thimble is a curved piece of metal that supports a loop of rope and protects it from sharp bends and abrasion. The ends of the loop are secured together with U-bolt clips. The *dead end* is the loose end of a rope arranged in a loop. The *live end* is the load-lifting portion of a rope arranged in a loop. A U-bolt clip consists of a saddle, a threaded U-section, and two nuts. The clip should be assembled with the threaded U-section contacting the dead end section, which prevents damage to the load-bearing section.

Clips must be arranged, spaced, and assembled properly to maintain the strength of the rope. **See Figure 2-14.** The required turnback length and number of clips is determined by the rope size and/or manufacturer's specifications. The first clip is placed approximately 4″ from the end of the rope and the nuts are tightened. The second clip is placed at the end of the thimble and the nuts are finger tightened. Any other clips are spaced evenly between the first two and finger tightened. Finally, a load is placed on the rope and the remaining nuts are alternately tightened. The efficiency of a loop and thimble attachment is approximately 80%.

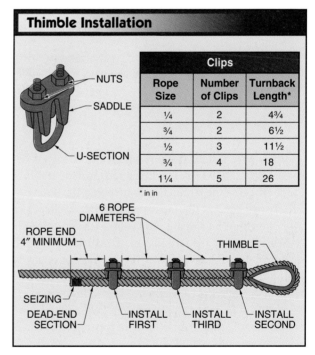

Thimble Installation

Clips		
Rope Size	Number of Clips	Turnback Length*
¼	2	4¾
⅜	2	6½
½	3	11½
¾	4	18
1¼	5	26

* in in

Figure 2-14. Thimbles are installed to form a loop and the ends of the wire rope are fastened with a specific number of clips.

Sockets. A *socket* is a rope attachment through which a rope end is terminated. Sockets provide closed or open fittings to which other hardware can be attached. Closed fittings are solid loops. Open fittings have a part that can be removed in order to connect it to a closed fitting.

Wire rope sockets include swage, spelter, and wedge designs. Swage and spelter sockets are permanent wire rope attachments. Permanent wire rope attachments have the highest efficiency ratings at 95% to 100%.

A *swage socket* is a socket that is compressed onto the end of a wire rope. **See Figure 2-15.** Swage sockets must be compressed in a hydraulic press to achieve the necessary binding to the rope. The inside of the socket conforms to the shape of the rope strands and locks it into place.

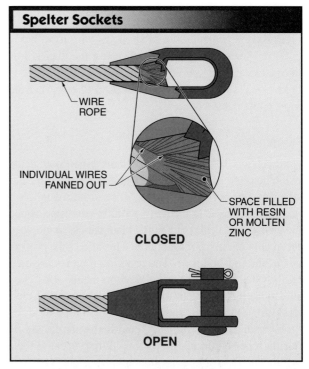

Figure 2-16. Spelter sockets are locked onto a wire rope end by a wedge formed out of the fanned-out wire encased in resin or zinc.

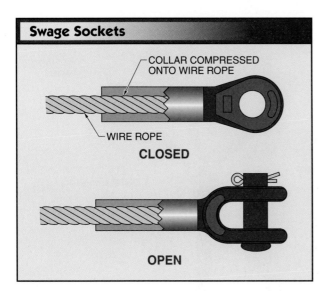

Figure 2-15. A swage socket is pressed onto the end of a wire rope with high pressure until the collar conforms to the shape of the rope.

A *spelter socket* is a socket that uses molten zinc or resin to secure the end of a wire rope inside the socket. **See Figure 2-16.** The rope end is inserted through the socket collar and the individual wires are separated and fanned out. Molten zinc or resin is poured into the collar and hardens around the wires, creating a solid wedge-shaped assembly that resists passing back through the socket.

A *wedge socket* is a socket that holds a loop of wire rope securely with a wedge that is tightened by tension on the rope. **See Figure 2-17.** Wedge sockets are popular because they can be installed and repositioned quickly and easily. However, because of its design, a wedge socket can be incorrectly installed, creating a sharp bend on the live end of the rope. The live end must be in line with the socket. The exposed dead-end section must extend out of the wedge a minimum of eight rope diameters.

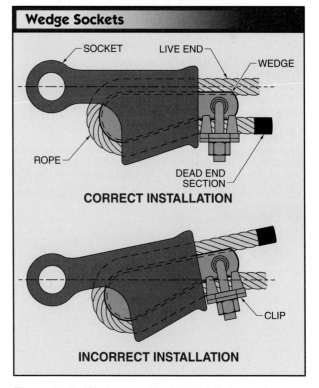

Figure 2-17. Wedge sockets hold tightly to a wire rope when it is tensioned.

FIBER ROPE

Fiber rope is generally not as strong as wire rope, but is preferred for some applications because the fiber is less likely to gouge or mar equipment surfaces. Fiber rope is broadly classified by the material used to construct the rope, either natural or synthetic.

Fibers

Natural fibers are processed from plants. Fibers used in the manufacturing of rope include manila, hemp, cotton, and sisal. Manila fiber can be used for lifting ropes, though sisal is sometimes used as a core material in wire rope. Since the growth and health of a living plant varies, so too does the quality of the harvested fibers. This affects the properties of the finished rope. The resulting rope is classified by the quality of fiber used. Common manila rope classifications include yacht rope, number 1, number 2, and hardware. Only yacht and number 1 should be used for lifting applications. Number 2 and hardware classes of manila rope should not be used for lifting because their quality and type of fiber is often unknown.

Synthetic materials used for lifting ropes include nylon, polypropylene, polyesters (such as Dacron®), and aramids (such as Kevlar®). Synthetic ropes are used more commonly today because of their consistent characteristics and special properties, such as chemical resistance. Also, the breaking strengths of synthetic fibers are far greater than those of manila fibers. **See Figure 2-18.** This is because a synthetic fiber is continuous throughout the length of the rope while the natural fibers are short lengths spun together. Another advantage of synthetic fibers is that they do not mildew, rot, or decay as natural fibers do.

Fiber Rope Construction

Laid fiber rope, similar to wire rope, is constructed by twisting fibers into yarn, yarn into strands, and strands into rope. **See Figure 2-19.** A yarn is made by twisting the fibers to the right. Several yarns are then twisted together to the left to create a strand. Three or more strands are then twisted to the right to create the rope. Reversing the twist of each step prevents the rope from unwinding. Laid fiber rope may or may not have a core.

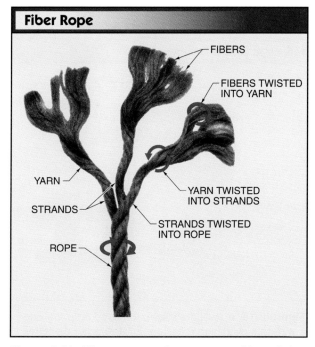

Figure 2-19. Fiber rope can be constructed by twisting fibers into yarn, yarn into strands, and strands into rope.

Breaking Strengths of Selected Fiber Ropes*								
Diameter†	Manila	Polypropylene	Polyester			Nylon		
	3-Strand Twisted	3-Strand Twisted	3-Strand Twisted	Double Braided	8-Strand Plaited	3-Strand Twisted	Double Braided	8-Strand Plaited
⅝	405	720	800	—	—	950	—	—
¾	540	1130	1200	1900	2000	1500	1785	1500
1	900	1710	2000	2935	3100	2600	2835	2500
1⅛	1215	2440	2800	4245	4500	3300	4095	3700
1¼	1575	3160	3800	5730	6000	4800	5355	5000
1½	2385	3780	5000	7500	7700	5800	7245	6400
1¾	3105	4600	6500	9450	9700	7600	9450	8000
2	3960	5600	8000	11,660	12,100	9800	12,600	11,000

* in lb
† in in.

Figure 2-18. Synthetic fiber ropes are generally stronger than natural fiber ropes, though the strength varies with construction type.

The *lay* is the length of rope in which a strand makes one complete spiral wrap. (This meaning for the term "lay" is in addition to the meaning indicating the direction of twist.) Lay length measurements are used to determine if the rope has stretched due to age or use. The initial measurement is made when the rope is new. This gives a comparison figure for all future measurements. Several whole lay lengths should be measured. For example, four complete lays of a rope may measure 1′-4″. If there is a measurable increase in lay length or a decrease in rope diameter of any rope, it should be removed from service.

Synthetic fiber rope can be constructed by braiding or plaiting, instead of twisting, the strands. **See Figure 2-20.** *Braiding* is the weaving of three or more untwisted strands into a rope. Various braiding patterns can be used to create hollow ropes, solid ropes, and wide ribbon-like bands.

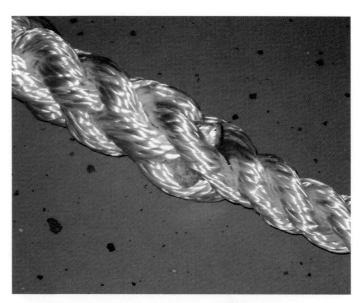

Two lengths of fiber rope can sometimes be spliced together without significant loss of strength.

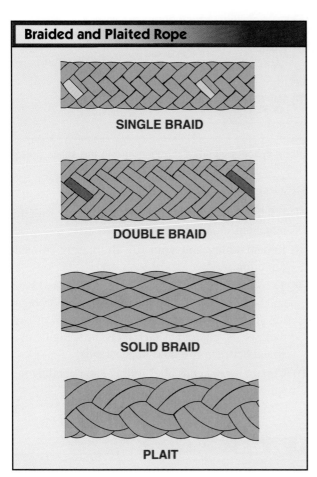

Braided and Plaited Rope

SINGLE BRAID

DOUBLE BRAID

SOLID BRAID

PLAIT

Figure 2-20. Synthetic fiber ropes can be constructed by braiding or plaiting the strands, which may or may not be twisted.

Single-braid rope consists of an even number of strands woven into a tube shape. This braid may be used to cover a core material, or the interior may be left void. Double-braid rope consists of completely separate inner and outer braids, which may be of different materials. Often, the inner material has greater strength while the outer material has better abrasion resistance. In both single and double braids, half the strands spiral in one direction while the other half spiral in the other. Alternatively, solid braid uses strands that all spiral in the same direction, but alternate between the inner and outer layers.

Plaiting is the weaving of four pairs of alternately twisted strands into a rope. Two right-hand pairs of strands are twisted to the left and two left-hand pairs are twisted to the right. This results in inherently non-rotating rope.

Fiber Rope Splicing

A *splice* is the braiding together of two portions of rope in order to form a permanent connection. Splices are commonly used to join the ends of two ropes of similar strength and thickness. **See Figure 2-21.** Ropes are spliced by unlaying a portion of each rope end and then braiding the loose strands of each into the twisted portion of the other rope. An *unlay* is the untwisting of the strands in a rope. The *standing part* is the portion of a rope that is unaltered or not involved in making a knot or hitch.

Long Splices

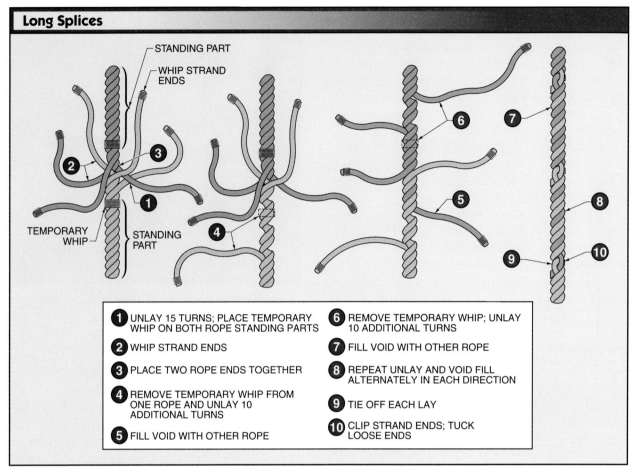

STANDING PART

WHIP STRAND ENDS

TEMPORARY WHIP

STANDING PART

1. UNLAY 15 TURNS; PLACE TEMPORARY WHIP ON BOTH ROPE STANDING PARTS

2. WHIP STRAND ENDS

3. PLACE TWO ROPE ENDS TOGETHER

4. REMOVE TEMPORARY WHIP FROM ONE ROPE AND UNLAY 10 ADDITIONAL TURNS

5. FILL VOID WITH OTHER ROPE

6. REMOVE TEMPORARY WHIP; UNLAY 10 ADDITIONAL TURNS

7. FILL VOID WITH OTHER ROPE

8. REPEAT UNLAY AND VOID FILL ALTERNATELY IN EACH DIRECTION

9. TIE OFF EACH LAY

10. CLIP STRAND ENDS; TUCK LOOSE ENDS

Figure 2-21. A splice is the permanent joining of two ropes. A long splice minimizes the increase to the splice area's diameter.

A short splice uses an unlay of six to eight rope strands on each rope. When braided together, a short splice increases the rope diameter, making it unsuitable for pulley use. A long splice uses an unlay of 15 turns and does not significantly increase the rope diameter. A long splice is formed using the following procedure:

1. Unlay 15 turns and place a temporary whip on the standing parts of both ropes.
2. Whip the strand ends.
3. Place the two rope ends (standing part terminations) together, alternating strands of one end with the strands of the other.
4. Remove the temporary whip from one rope and unlay one strand about 10 additional turns.
5. Fill the void in the grooves of the 10 turns with the matching strand of the other rope.
6. Remove the temporary whip from the other rope and unlay 10 additional turns.
7. Fill the void in the grooves of the 10 turns with the matching strand of the other rope.
8. Repeat unlay and void fill alternately in each direction.
9. Tie off each lay of strands using an overhand knot and begin tucking the strand from one rope through the strands of the other rope. A minimum of two tuck sets is required. A *tuck set* is the wedging of a strand between two other rope strands.
10. Clip the strand ends after rolling and pounding the splice.

> **⚡ Factoid**
>
> A splice can retain up to 95% of the original strength of a rope. When joining rope, splices are preferred over knots, which can reduce rope strength by as much as 50%.

Splices are also used to join portions of the same rope. An *eye loop* is a splice that forms a loop at the end of a rope. Eye loops typically contain a thimble for protecting the rope. **See Figure 2-22.** The thimble is inserted after the splice is completed and is held in place by whipping. An eye loop is formed using the following procedure:

1. Unlay four turns of strands. Place a temporary whip on the standing part and whip the strand ends.

2. Form the eye of thimble size.

3. Tuck strand 1 through the standing part at 90° to the lay of the rope.

4. Tuck strand 2 through the standing part in the same direction.

5. Turn the assembly over and tuck strand 3 through the standing part.

6. Alternately tuck each strand through the standing part. Trim ends.

7. Remove the temporary whipping. Insert thimble and add whipping.

⚡ Factoid

When forming knots, hitches, or splices, the working part is the portion of rope that includes the loose ends that are being manipulated. The standing part is the portion that is fixed. The standing part typically encompasses the majority of the rope length.

Eye Loops

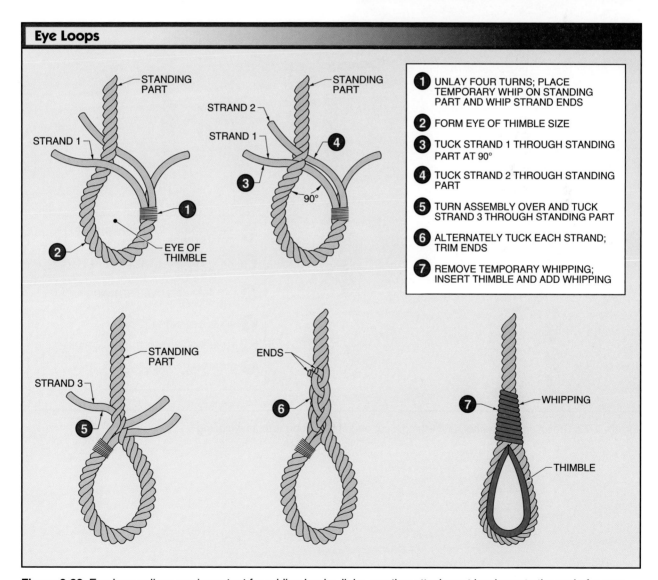

STANDING PART

STRAND 1

① EYE OF THIMBLE

②

STANDING PART

STRAND 2

STRAND 1

④

③

90°

STANDING PART

STRAND 3

⑤

ENDS

⑥

⑦ WHIPPING

THIMBLE

① UNLAY FOUR TURNS; PLACE TEMPORARY WHIP ON STANDING PART AND WHIP STRAND ENDS

② FORM EYE OF THIMBLE SIZE

③ TUCK STRAND 1 THROUGH STANDING PART AT 90°

④ TUCK STRAND 2 THROUGH STANDING PART

⑤ TURN ASSEMBLY OVER AND TUCK STRAND 3 THROUGH STANDING PART

⑥ ALTERNATELY TUCK EACH STRAND; TRIM ENDS

⑦ REMOVE TEMPORARY WHIPPING; INSERT THIMBLE AND ADD WHIPPING

Figure 2-22. Eye-loop splices are important for adding hooks, links, or other attachment hardware to the end of a rope.

Crowning is a splice that finishes a rope end by braiding its loose strands back on itself. Crowning is an alternative to whipping when an enlarged rope end is desired or not objectionable. **See Figure 2-23.** A rope crown termination is formed using the following procedure:

1. Unlay rope ends eight turns and whip the strand ends.

2. For a three-strand rope, loop strand 1 and lay strand 2 over strand 1 and down the side of the rope.

3. Lay strand 3 over strand 2 and through strand 1 loop.

4. Snug strands 1, 2, and 3.

5. Tuck strand 1 through strand 2 of the standing part of the rope.

6. Alternately tuck each strand. Trim ends. The crown of the rope becomes tighter with time and use.

⚡ **Factoid**

Crowning is a method of terminating a length of fiber rope without whipping. It resists unraveling even through wear that might otherwise break whipping twine. However, it slightly increases rope diameter.

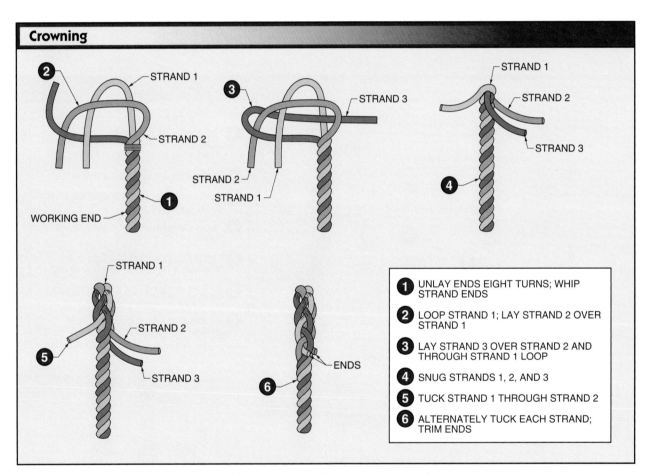

Crowning

1. UNLAY ENDS EIGHT TURNS; WHIP STRAND ENDS

2. LOOP STRAND 1; LAY STRAND 2 OVER STRAND 1

3. LAY STRAND 3 OVER STRAND 2 AND THROUGH STRAND 1 LOOP

4. SNUG STRANDS 1, 2, AND 3

5. TUCK STRAND 1 THROUGH STRAND 2

6. ALTERNATELY TUCK EACH STRAND; TRIM ENDS

Figure 2-23. Crowning is a method of finishing a cut end of fiber rope without whipping.

Slings 3

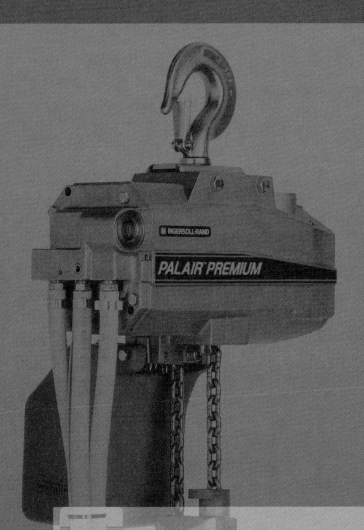

The rigging of a load for lifting may use any of a variety of sling types. Besides rope and rope slings, commonly used equipment includes web slings, round slings, and chain. Many rigging scenarios can use any of these types of equipment, but some situations require the special characteristics of one type. Web slings and round slings are entirely composed of synthetic fibers. They are very strong, yet gentle on easily damaged loads and resistant to many chemical environments. Chain makes extremely strong and durable slings that can be used in a wide range of temperatures. All sling types use attachment hardware, including hooks, shackles, and master links.

Objectives

- Describe the construction of webbing and web slings.
- Identify the factors that affect web sling strength.
- Compare the construction of round slings to web slings.
- Describe the material characteristics and construction of chain.
- Identify the grades of chain appropriate for rigging and tie-down applications.
- List the common types of sling attachments and describe their uses.

WEB SLINGS

A *web sling* is a flat rigging sling made from synthetic webbing material. *Webbing* is flat narrow strapping woven from yarns of strong synthetic fibers. **See Figure 3-1.** Webbing material is relatively soft and distributes pressure across a wide surface, making it ideal for rigging easily damaged loads. It is often used with glass or loads with polished or painted surfaces.

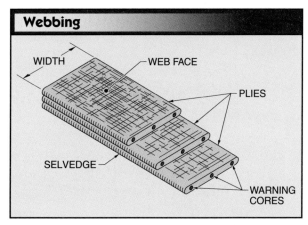

Webbing

Figure 3-1. Webbing material consists of synthetic fibers woven into wide, flat straps. Multiple layers, or plies, can be sewn together to make stronger webbing.

Webbing

Webbing for rigging purposes is made of woven nylon or polyester fibers. Colored marker yarns woven into the center of the face of the webbing may be used to identify the material. Nylon webbing is plain or has black markers. Polyester has blue markers. Manufacturers may also use colored marker yarns at the edges to indicate other construction types.

Most web-sling damage starts on the edge, so webbing includes selvedges. A *selvedge* is an edge treatment on woven material that prevents unraveling. The selvedge is formed from yarns that zigzag across the width of the webbing, exposing only a turn of the continuous yarn at the edges. **See Figure 3-2.** The weave is often drawn tighter at the edge to strengthen the edge.

In some cases, special brightly colored yarns are woven into the webbing core. If webbing material is worn away or torn enough to expose these yarns, the wear is excessive and the webbing is no longer safe to use. Webbing must be removed from service if these warning yarns become visible.

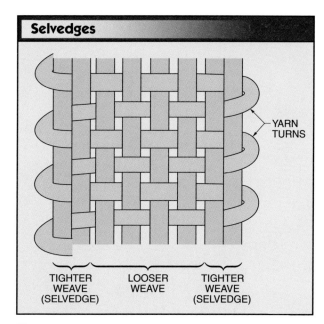

Selvedges

Figure 3-2. Webbing is woven with selvedges to protect the weave from unraveling.

The synthetic fibers used in webbing are generally very resistant to chemicals. **See Figure 3-3.** Polyester is resistant to many acids, and nylon is resistant to most alkalis. Both are resistant to oils, detergents, water, and solvents. However, certain chemicals and environmental conditions may still cause degradation, so it is critical to consult the manufacturer when selecting a web sling to be used in chemically active areas. The chemical resistance of a sling is also influenced by the material of the end fittings.

General Chemical Resistance for Webbing Material		
Chemical	**Polyester**	**Nylon**
Acids	Most	No
Alcohols	Yes	Yes
Aldehydes	No	Yes
Alkalis, Strong	Some	Yes
Alkalis, Weak	Yes	Yes
Bleaching Agents	Yes	No
Dry Cleaning Solvents	Yes	Yes
Ethers	Yes	Yes
Hydrocarbons	Yes	Yes
Ketones	Yes	Yes
Oils	Yes	Yes
Soap/Detergents	Yes	Yes
Water/Seawater	Yes	Yes

Figure 3-3. An advantage of web slings is that synthetic fibers are resistant to many types of chemicals.

Exposure to ultraviolet light, such as from sunlight or arc welding, may affect the material strength without any visible indication. Also, both polyester and nylon are seriously degraded at temperatures above 200°F (392°C).

Webbing is available in multiple plies (layers). The number of plies determines the duty rating of webbing. Each ply supports some of the load, making multiple-ply webbing stronger. Web slings are available in one- to four-ply construction and with widths ranging from 1″ to 12″. Generally, web slings are constructed of one or two plies. Three- or four-ply slings are used only in special conditions.

Web-Sling Construction

Web-sling components consist of length, body, splice, and loop eye. **See Figure 3-4.** The *web sling length* is the distance between the ends of a web sling, including any fittings. The *web sling body* is the portion of the sling that is between the loop eyes or end fittings (if any).

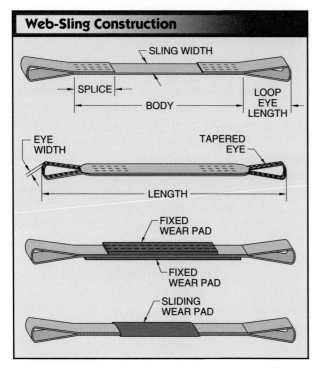

Figure 3-4. Webbing is sewn into slings by splicing and forming loop eyes.

A *splice* is an overlap of webbing material that is sewn together. The *loop eye* is a length of webbing folded back and spliced to the sling body, forming a closed loop. The length of the loop eye varies for the

width of the sling webbing. When full-width sling loop eyes are too wide to properly fit into a hoist hook, a web sling with tapered loop eyes is used. The webbing is folded to a narrower width at its bearing point to accommodate the hardware.

Wear pads are another common component of web slings. A *wear pad* is a leather or webbed pad used to protect the web sling from damage. Wear pads are either sewn to the webbing or slide along the body, allowing adjustable protection.

Web slings are fabricated in at least six standard configuration types. **See Figure 3-5.** Manufacturers may offer additional configurations for specialized applications.

- Type 1 is a web sling made with a triangle fitting on one end and a large slotted choker fitting on the other end. This type of sling is also known as a triangle-choker (TC) sling. Type 1 web slings are typically used for choker hitches, though they are also suitable for vertical and basket hitches.
- Type 2 is a web sling made with a triangle fitting on both ends, so it is also known as a triangle-triangle (TT) sling. Type 2 web slings are used for vertical or basket hitches.
- Type 3 is a web sling made with large flat loops at each end that are in the same plane as the body. It is also known as an eye-eye (EE) sling. Type 3 web slings are used for vertical or basket hitches, or for a choker hitch by passing one eye around the load and through the other eye. Type 3 web slings are often available with tapered eyes to permit their use with hooks.
- Type 4 is a web sling made with both eyes twisted to form loop eyes that are at right angles to the plane of the sling body. This arrangement makes a better choker hitch than the Type 3 style, though these slings can also be used for vertical and basket hitches.
- Type 5 is an endless web sling made by joining the ends with a load-bearing splice. It is also known as a grommet sling. Type 5 web slings are used for numerous applications and are the most widely used. Because they have an endless design, they may be used in basket, vertical, or choker hitch applications.
- Type 6 is an endless web sling with butted edges sewn together to form a body and two loop eyes, which are at right angles to the plane of the body. It is also known as a reverse eye (RE) sling because the eyes are formed by folding the sling in an opposing direction than Type 3 and Type 4 eyes. A wear pad is often added on one side or both sides of the sling body. Type 6 web slings are used for rugged service, such as lifting irregularly shaped objects like stone.

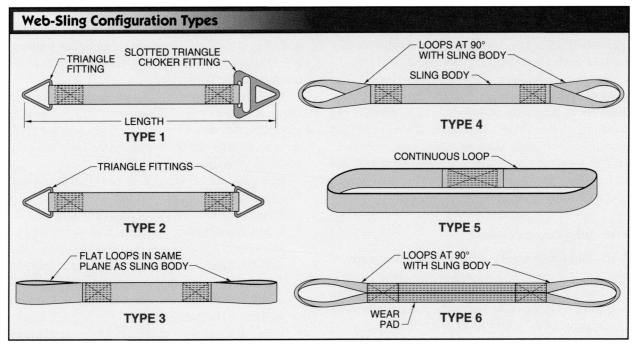

Figure 3-5. There are six primary web-sling configurations, which are available in various sizes and webbing types.

Web-Sling Strength

Web-sling load capacity tables generally list the capacity rating (working load limits) for various webbing classes, webbing width, number of plies, and sling types. **See Figure 3-6.** These values are calculated based on the webbing material strength, fabrication efficiency, and safety factor.

Webbing material is broadly classified as Class 5 or Class 7 for its breaking strength. Breaking strength is determined by its fiber material, thickness, and construction. Class 5 webbing has a minimum certified tensile strength of 6800 lb/in. of width per ply. Class 7 webbing has a minimum certified tensile strength of 9800 lb/in. of width per ply. Either class of webbing may be manufactured into single- or multiple-ply webbing.

Fabrication efficiency is the ratio of the tensile strength of a webbing material to the tensile strength of the web sling it is fabricated into. Fabrication efficiency accounts for the loss of strength in the webbing due to stitching and other modifications. Typical fabrication efficiencies are 80% to 85% for single-ply slings but are lower for multiple-ply or very wide slings.

The safety factor determines the fraction of total tensile strength that may be used for lifting loads. The typical safety factor is 5. For unusual circumstances, safety factors are increased to 8 or more.

Web-sling manufacturers calculate the rated capacity (working load limit) for vertical hitches from the webbing strength, fabrication efficiency, and a safety factor of 5. This limit is then used to determine capacities of choker and basket hitches. Rated capacity information is also printed on durable tags sewn onto the web sling.

Web-sling strength is based on new webbing material. Web-sling strength is decreased by age and mishandling, such as dragging the web sling on the floor, tying it in knots, pulling it from under a load when the load is resting on the webbing, or dropping the metal fittings. Bunching webbing material between the ears of a clevis, shackle, or hook also weakens web-sling strength.

ROUND SLINGS

A *round sling* is an endless (continuous loop) sling consisting of unwoven synthetic fiber yarns enclosed in a protective cover. Round slings make excellent choker-hitch slings because they are extremely flexible and conform to the shape of the load. Also, due to their construction, choker hitches do not bind or lock up, making sling release simple.

Rated Capacities of Web Slings in Vertical Hitches*

Plies	Width†	Class 5 Webbing		Class 7 Webbing	
		Types 1, 2, 3, and 4	Type 5	Types 1, 2, 3, and 4	Type 5
1 Ply	1	1100	2200	1600	3200
	2	2200	4400	3100	6200
	3	3300	6600	4700	9400
	4	4400	8800	6200	12,400
	6	6600	13,200	9300	18,600
	8	—	—	11,800	21,200
	10	—	—	14,700	26,500
	12	—	—	17,600	31,800
2 Ply	1	2200	4400	3100	6200
	2	4400	8800	6200	12,400
	3	6600	13,200	8800	17,600
	4	8200	16,400	11,000	22,000
	6	12,300	24,600	16,500	33,000
	8	—	—	22,700	42,300
	10	—	—	28,400	52,900
	12	—	—	34,100	63,500
4 Ply	1	Not Typically Available	Not Typically Available	5500	11,000
	2			11,000	22,000
	3			16,400	32,900
	4			20,400	40,800
	6			30,600	61,200

* in lb, with a safety factor of 5. Type 6 rated capacities vary by manufacturer.
† in in.

Figure 3-6. The rated capacity of a web sling depends on the webbing class, number of plies, webbing width, and sling construction type.

Round-Sling Construction

The core yarns, typically polyester, are uniformly wound to ensure even load-bearing distribution. **See Figure 3-7.** The cover is made from polyester or nylon fibers woven into a continuous tubular shape. The cover provides protection to the core and is not load bearing.

A round sling is similar to Type 5 endless web sling when used as a choker or basket hitch. Additional sleeves may be placed over the round sling to offer extra abrasion protection or to create a loop eye at each end (eye-eye design). Round slings are also manufactured with fittings or coupling components. Bridle slings are assembled during manufacture by including more than one round-sling leg to a master link.

⚡ **Factoid**

Webbing is also used as tie-downs to secure cargo. A tie-down includes a ratchet-type tightener in addition to fittings at each end of the webbing.

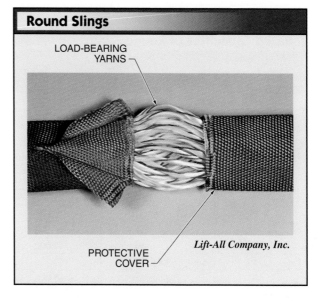

Round Slings

LOAD-BEARING YARNS

PROTECTIVE COVER

Lift-All Company, Inc.

Figure 3-7. A round sling is composed of a bundle of un-woven yarns of load-bearing synthetic fibers, surrounded by a non-load-bearing woven cover.

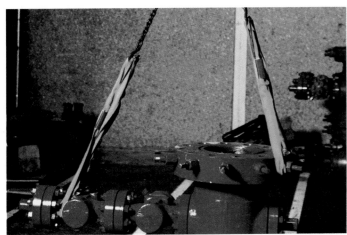

Lift-All Company, Inc.
Round slings are often used to lift unusual shapes or loads with painted finishes.

Round-Sling Strength

The rated capacity (working load limit) of a round sling is listed on its identification tag and indicated by the color of its cover. The color codes may vary by manufacturer, though most follow a common sequence. **See Figure 3-8.** Identification tags carry the rated capacities for vertical hitches, choker hitches, and vertical basket hitches, along with manufacturer and sling construction information. A round sling is not to be used with a load greater than the working load limit marked on its identification tag. Any round sling that has a missing or unreadable identification tag should be removed from service.

CHAIN

A *chain* is a series of metal links connected to one another to form a continuous line. **See Figure 3-9.** Chain is recommended for rugged industrial applications where flexibility, abrasion resistance, and long life are required. Chain can often be used in situations in which other materials would be damaged by the load or environment, such as rough or raw castings or high temperatures.

Chain

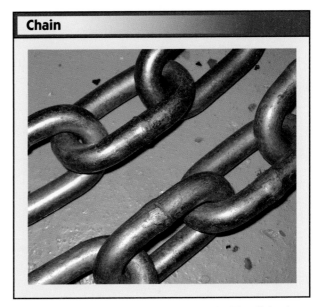

Figure 3-9. Chain is formed into interlocking links from steel rod.

Rated Capacities of Round Slings*					
Round Sling Size	Color Code	Sling Hitch			
		Vertical	Choker	Vertical Basket	45° Basket
1	Purple	2600	2100	5200	3700
2	Green	5300	4200	10,600	7500
3	Yellow	8400	6700	16,800	11,900
4	Tan	10,600	8500	21,200	15,000
5	Red	13,200	10,600	26,400	18,700
6	White	16,800	13,400	33,600	23,800
7	Blue	21,200	17,000	42,400	30,000
8	Orange	25,000	20,000	50,000	35,400
9	Orange	31,000	24,800	62,000	43,800
10	Orange	40,000	32,000	80,000	56,600
11	Orange	53,000	42,400	106,000	74,900
12	Orange	66,000	52,800	132,000	93,000

* in lb

Figure 3-8. The rated capacity of a round sling can usually be identified by the color of its cover, which corresponds to certain working load limits.

The use of chain for rigging is normally favored over wire rope because chain has approximately three times the impact-absorption capability of wire rope and is more flexible. Also, wire rope costs more than chain of similar strength and has only 5% of the expected service life.

Chain Construction

The strength of chain and chain attachments depends on the steel alloys from which they are made. An *alloy* is metal formulated from the combination of two or more elements. The alloy composition and heat-treating processes determine the metal's strength, hardness, and other characteristics.

A chain is formed from steel rod that is cut into short lengths. Each piece is held against a forming die while rollers bend the rod around into a link shape, with the ends meeting on a long side. The next piece of rod is inserted through the link and rolled into the same shape. The links are then welded together and given various surface treatments for finish or corrosion resistance.

Rigging or hoisting chain is designed to deform before fracturing. A *fracture* is a crack in metal caused by the stress and fatigue of repeated pulling or bending forces. Sling chain is capable of 15% to 30% elongation before breaking. However, chain should be removed from service if elongation exceeds about 5% or the thickness of any part of a link has decreased by about 10%. **See Figure 3-10.**

Chain Strength

The National Association of Chain Manufacturers (NACM), in conjunction with the International Organization for Standardization (ISO), develops programs to standardize materials and processes for chain. Of the many types of chain specified, only Grade 80 and Grade 100 chain are to be used for sling or tie-down applications. These chains offer high strength, wear resistance, and durability. **See Figure 3-11.**

> ### ⚡ Factoid
> Steel hardness depends on the temperatures used during manufacturing and the rate at which the steel is allowed to cool. Hardness is measured with a Brinell hardness tester. A Brinell hardness (HB) number quantifies hardness from approximately 150 HB for soft metal to 750 HB for hardened metal. The steel in a typical sling chain varies from 250 HB to 450 HB.

Grade 80 and Grade 100 chains must include embossed identifying numbers at intervals no greater than 3′. The characters must be raised and include a manufacturer's mark, traceability or date code, and grade indicator. Grade 80 chain is indicated by "8", "80", or "800". Grade 100 chain is indicated by "10", "100", or "1000".

Chain Deformation

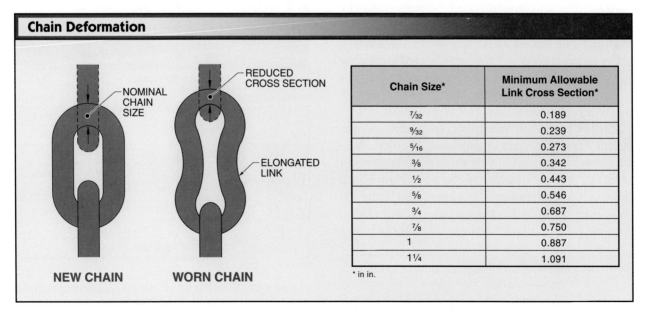

Chain Size*	Minimum Allowable Link Cross Section*
7/32	0.189
9/32	0.239
5/16	0.273
3/8	0.342
1/2	0.443
5/8	0.546
3/4	0.687
7/8	0.750
1	0.887
1 1/4	1.091

* in in.

Figure 3-10. The links of a chain that has been overloaded and worn become elongated and thinner in cross section.

Rated Capacities of Chain*

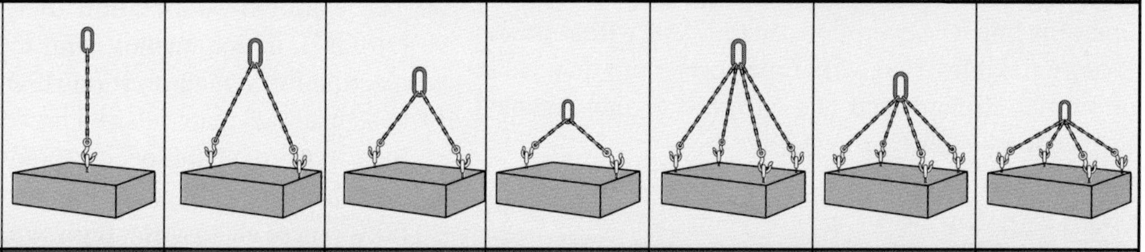

Grade	Chain Size†	90° Vertical Load	60° Vertical Load	45° Vertical Load	30° Vertical Load	60° Quad Leg Load	45° Quad Leg Load	30° Quad Leg Load
80	7/32	2100	3600	3000	2100	5450	4450	3150
	9/32	3500	6100	4900	3500	9100	7400	5200
	3/8	7100	12,300	10,000	7100	18,400	15,100	10,600
	1/2	12,000	20,800	17,000	12,000	31,200	25,500	18,000
	5/8	18,100	31,300	25,600	18,100	47,000	38,400	27,100
	3/4	28,300	49,000	40,000	28,300	73,500	60,000	42,400
	7/8	34,200	59,200	48,400	34,200	88,900	72,500	51,300
	1	47,700	82,600	67,400	47,700	123,900	101,200	71,500
	1 1/4	72,300	125,200	102,200	72,300	187,800	153,400	108,400
100	7/32	2700	4700	3800	2700	7000	5700	4000
	9/32	4300	7400	6100	4300	11,200	9100	6400
	3/8	8800	15,200	12,400	8800	22,900	18,700	13,200
	1/2	15,000	26,000	21,200	15,000	39,000	31,800	22,500
	5/8	22,600	39,100	32,000	22,600	58,700	47,900	33,900
	3/4	35,300	61,100	49,900	35,300	91,700	74,900	53,000

* in lb
† in in.

Figure 3-11. The rated capacity of chain is determined by the diameter of the rod that forms the links. This rating can then be applied to different sling arrangements to determine maximum lifting capacity.

For a particular grade, working load limits are based on nominal chain size. Nominal chain size is designated by the diameter of the rod used to form the links during the manufacturing process. Depending on the manufacturer, safety factors between 3.5 and 5 may be used to calculate the working load limit from the breaking strength. This information must be verified from the manufacturer in case a different safety factor should be used.

Chain is particularly suited for high-temperature applications where other types of slings cannot be used. However, extreme temperatures are still a consideration that affects the working load limit of chain. **See Figure 3-12.** Extremely low temperatures make the metal brittle and more likely to fracture. High temperatures soften the metal, reducing the load capacity, perhaps permanently.

Factoid

The chain included with a hoist may not display a grade number because it is designed for the hoist mechanisms. However, its strength is at least as strong as the hoist's rating.

Reduction of Chain Capacity Due to Temperature

Chain Temperature*	While at Temperature		Permanently	
	Grade 80	Grade 100	Grade 80	Grade 100
Below −40	Do not use	Do not use	None	None
Below −20	None	Do not use	None	None
400	10%	15%	None	None
500	15%	25%	None	5%
600	20%	30%	5%	15%
700	30%	40%	10%	20%
800	40%	50%	15%	25%
900	50%	60%	20%	30%
1000	60%	70%	25%	35%
Over 1000	Remove from service			

* in °F

Figure 3-12. Chain can be used at far greater temperatures than most other sling materials, but is still subject to loss of lifting capacity at extreme conditions.

SLING ATTACHMENTS

Typical connecting attachments between the load, rigging, and hoisting device include shackles, master links, and hooks. These devices allow connections between loads and slings, slings and other slings, and slings and hoists.

Some attachments are added when the sling is manufactured. In this case, the rated capacity of the entire sling should already account for the strength of the attachments. However, various attachments can be purchased separately and individually attached. A rigging assembly is only as strong as its weakest component, so the strength of added attachments and hardware must be considered. Attachments must be used for their intended purpose and in accordance with the manufacturer's instructions. Never use makeshift hooks, links, or fasteners since their strengths are unknown.

Hooks

A hook is usually the primary link between the rigged load and the hoisting equipment. A *hook* is a curved implement used for temporarily connecting rigging to loads or lifting equipment. Hooks are made in various designs and sizes. The primary design variations are based on the hook shape, method of attachment, and latch arrangement. Hooks are available in many combinations of these designs. **See Figure 3-13.**

The Crosby Group, Inc.
Whenever possible, hooks should include some means, such as a latch, to prevent slings from accidentally slipping out of the hook.

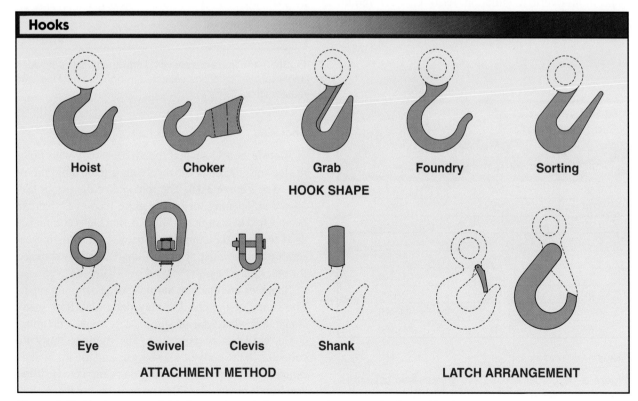

Figure 3-13. Hooks are available in a variety of shapes, attachment methods, and latch arrangements.

The most common hook design is the hoist hook. A *hoist hook* is a hook with a rounded shape that is suitable for most rigging and lifting applications. Other hook shapes are used for special applications. A *choker hook* is a sliding hook used to form a choker sling when hooked to a sling eye. A *grab hook* is a hook that can engage and securely hold a chain link. This type of hook can be used to shorten a chain sling leg. A *foundry hook* is a hook with a wide, deep throat that fits the handles of molds or castings. A *sorting hook* is a hook with a straight, tapered tip that can be used to directly hold plates, cylinders, and other shapes that allow full engagement.

Swivel hardware allows the load to turn without damaging or twisting the chain. A regular swivel hook is used only as an aid for hook positioning and is not intended for load rotation. Special load-rotation swivel hooks are available for such applications. Hooks with latches or gates prevent the sudden release of loads due to shifting.

Hooks are normally made of forged alloy steel. Hook size is chosen for the strength rating. **See Figure 3-14.** The working load limit must be sufficient to lift the load but still be the weakest member of the hoisting equipment. This is so that the hook is the first to bend in an overload situation. Also, heat can reduce the strength of a hook, so they should never be heated above 800°F.

Hooks must be attached to loads in such a way that the hooks are fully engaged and loaded in line. The load should be supported from the bowl of the hook. When used at angles other than vertical, the tip of the hook must point outward in order to reduce the chance that the hook will slip off the lift point.

When a hook is used to collect two slings, the maximum included angle is 90°. **See Figure 3-15.** Some manufacturers include 45° (measured from vertical) angle marks on the hook to ensure compliance. For collecting more than two slings, shackles or master links must be used.

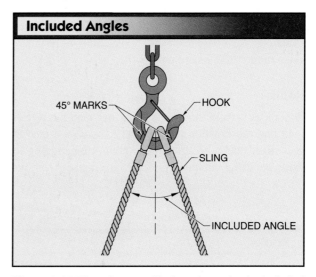

Figure 3-15. There is a specified maximum for the included angle formed by slings collected in hooks, shackles, and master links.

Shackles

A *shackle* is a U-shaped metal connector with holes drilled into the ends for receiving a removable pin or bolt. **See Figure 3-16.** The removal of the pin or bolt allows an opening for one or more loop eyes that can be attached to complete a sling. A shackle is commonly used to make the connection between the rigging assembly and the hoisting hook, though it can also be used for other purposes.

Shackles are made in various shapes and pin types. The shape of the shackle may determine how many slings and what type of slings (wire rope, web sling, chain, etc.) can be collected. The rigging slings are collected in the body of the shackle, and the lift hook is centered on the pin. When only one sling is to be lifted the shackle pin may be either up or down, but the shackle must be oriented straight along the direction of pull.

Rated Capacities of Eye Hoist Hooks

Throat Opening*	Working Load Limit†	
	Carbon Steel	Alloy Steel
0.88	1500	2000
0.97	2000	3000
1.00	3000	4000
1.12	4000	6000
1.36	6000	10,000
1.50	10,000	14,000
1.75	15,000	22,000
1.91	20,000	30,000
2.75	30,000	44,000

* in in.
† in lb, with a safety factor of 5

Figure 3-14. Larger hooks have greater load capacities. However, hooks are often identified by their rated capacities (sometimes in tons), rather than size.

Shackles

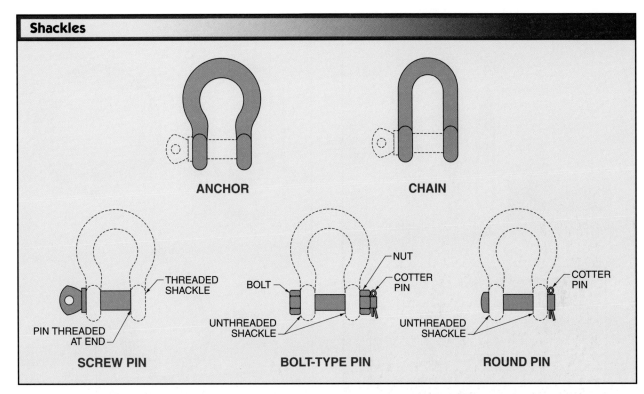

Figure 3-16. The most common shackle shapes are the anchor and chain types. Shackle pin designs include screw pins, bolt-type pins, and round pins, though round pins may not be appropriate for lifting applications.

Screw-pin shackles have threaded pins that are screwed into a threaded hole in the far end of the shackle. These shackles are appropriate for a variety of temporary rigging applications. However, they should not be used in any configuration where the movement of the load could cause the pin to unscrew. Bolt-type shackles use a bolt for a pin that is passed through both unthreaded ends of the shackle and secured with a nut and cotter pin. Bolt-type shackles are used for a variety of more permanent rigging applications. Round-pin shackles, which use only a cotter pin to secure the main pin, cannot be used for any side loading and may not be allowed for other applications.

Like chain links, shackle strength is determined by its steel composition, heat treatment process, and size. The size is the diameter of the material forming the bow of the shackle. **See Figure 3-17.** The maximum included angle for shackles collecting two or more slings is 120°.

The capacity rating assumes loading from a direction opposite the pin. In some circumstances, a shackle can be loaded from a side, but this reduces its working load limit. **See Figure 3-18.**

Rated Capacities of Anchor Shackles

Nominal Size*	Inside Width at Pin*	Pin Diameter*	Working Load Limit†	
			Carbon Steel	Alloy Steel
³⁄₁₆	0.38	0.25	667	—
¼	0.47	0.31	1000	—
⁵⁄₁₆	0.53	0.38	1500	—
⅜	0.66	0.44	2000	4000
⁷⁄₁₆	0.75	0.50	3000	5200
½	0.81	0.63	4000	6600
⅝	1.06	0.75	6500	10,000
¾	1.25	0.88	9500	14,000
⅞	1.44	1.00	13,000	19,000
1	1.69	1.13	17,000	25,000
1⅛	1.81	1.25	19,000	30,000
1¼	2.03	1.38	24,000	36,000
1⅜	2.25	1.50	27,000	42,000
1½	2.38	1.63	34,000	60,000

* in in.
† in lb, with a safety factor of 5

Figure 3-17. Shackles are identified by their size, inside width, and pin diameter. Larger shackles provide greater load lifting capacity.

Shackles Loaded at an Angle

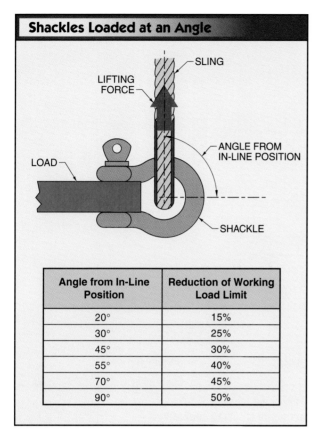

Angle from In-Line Position	Reduction of Working Load Limit
20°	15%
30°	25%
45°	30%
55°	40%
70°	45%
90°	50%

Figure 3-18. When shackles are used in a way that applies force at an angle, the working load limit is reduced.

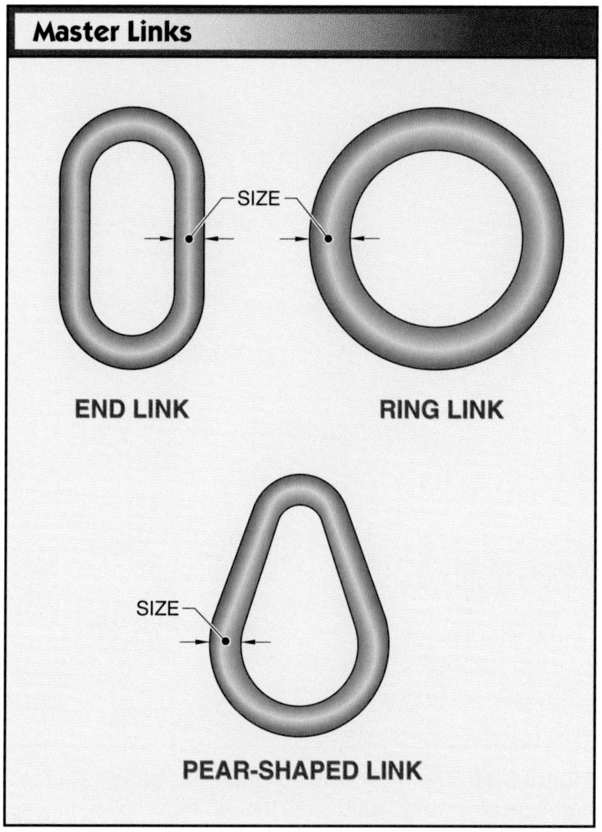

Master Links

A *master link* is a continuous link used to gather multiple slings and connect them to lift hooks. **See Figure 3-19.** A master link resembles a chain link but is larger to allow for multiple sling attachments and the insertion of a hook. Master links are often preattached to manufactured slings. Ring and pear-shaped master links that accommodate shackles or large hooks are also available. Master link working load limits are based on a single vertical load or a collection of sling legs with an included angle of 120° or less. **See Figure 3-20.**

⚡ Factoid

Sling assemblies that combine multiple lengths of chain (or other types of slings) with a master link at one end are commonly available. The master link is connected to the lifting device and the other ends are connected to the load's lift points. These assemblies make it easy to quickly rig a load with two, three, or four sling legs.

Master Links

END LINK   RING LINK

SIZE

PEAR-SHAPED LINK

Figure 3-19. Master links are used to collect multiple slings and connect rigging to lifting equipment.

Rated Capacities of Master Links*

Nominal Size*	Working Load Limit†			
	End	Ring	Pear Shape	
	Alloy Steel	Carbon Steel	Alloy Steel	Carbon Steel
½	7000	—	7000	2900
⅝	9000	—	9000	4200
¾	12,300	—	12,300	6000
⅞	15,000	7200	15,000	8300
1	24,360	10,800	24,360	10,800
1⅛	—	10,400	30,600	—
1¼	36,000	17,000	36,000	16,750
1⅜	—	19,000	43,000	20,500
1½	54,300	—	54,300	—
1⅝	—	—	62,600	—
1¾	84,900	—	84,900	—
2	102,600	—	102,600	—

* in in.
† in lb, with a safety factor of 5

Figure 3-20. Rated capacities for master links are based on the thickness of the link material.

4

Rigging Equipment Handling

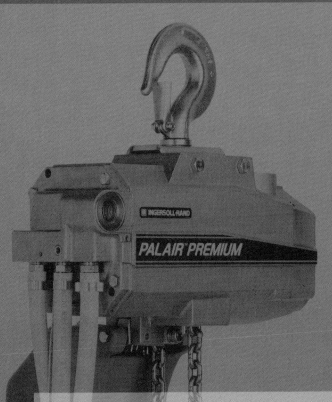

The possibility of rigging equipment failure is such a significant safety issue that the proper handling and inspection of the equipment is of utmost importance. Rigging equipment should be kept clean, dry, organized, and stored away from other equipment. Inspections must be frequent and thorough in order to identify signs of wear and damage that indicate loss of strength in the equipment. Damaged equipment must then be immediately removed from service so that it does not cause a safety hazard. Damaged equipment is usually destroyed because most types of damage cannot be adequately repaired.

Objectives

- Describe the procedure for handling damaged or defective equipment.
- Compare the types of rigging equipment inspections.
- Identify common signs of damage or excessive wear on wire rope.
- Identify common signs of damage or excessive wear on fiber rope.
- Identify common signs of damage or excessive wear on web slings and round slings.
- Identify common signs of damage or excessive wear on chain.
- Identify common signs of damage or excessive wear on attachments.
- Describe the proper storage recommendations for rigging equipment.
- Identify the recommended information to include on inspection documents.

RIGGING EQUIPMENT INSPECTION

Maintenance of rigging equipment includes inspection, recordkeeping, and storage. This does not include making temporary repairs to rope, webbing, or chains because it should never be attempted. Damaged equipment must be removed from service, stored separately, and tagged with a warning against use. **See Figure 4-1.** Depending on the damage, some equipment can be returned to the manufacturer for repair. Nonrepairable equipment should be promptly destroyed.

Damaged Equipment Tagging

Figure 4-1. Damaged rigging equipment that is no longer suitable for service must be tagged so that it is not inadvertently used.

All rigging equipment should be examined before being placed in service, before each use, and at periodic intervals. The initial inspection ensures that the equipment meets the required specifications for the expected loads and lifting conditions. Frequent inspections by rigging technicians before each use ensure that there is no obvious damage and that any identification or specification tags are still in place and readable. **See Figure 4-2.** Periodic inspections are more thorough and are conducted by designated individuals that are specifically trained in rigging equipment inspection.

Lift-All Company, Inc.
All rigging slings and hardware must be regularly inspected for wear or damage, which can significantly weaken the equipment and cause a safety hazard.

The frequency of periodic inspection is determined by the service conditions and rate of use. Past experience with similar equipment may influence the frequency of periodic inspections. However, periodic inspection of rigging equipment must be conducted at least annually, with the exception of round slings, which must be inspected at least monthly. Inspections must be timed so that equipment is removed from service before its condition poses a hazard with continued operation.

The full lengths of ropes and sling materials should be inspected carefully, though certain areas require extra attention. Sections of rope with frequent loading and bending (such as over pulleys or around loads) are particularly prone to failure due to fatigue. Points along a sling that are often in contact with pulleys or fittings when loaded are under greater stress. Ends that terminate at fittings are prone to having increased stress and holding moisture, which can cause mildew or corrosion.

⚡ **Factoid**

In relation to rigging equipment inspections, the terms "frequent" and "periodic" have particular meanings and should be used appropriately. Frequent inspections are quick checks performed just prior to each use. Periodic inspections are thorough inspections performed at regular intervals, such as every week or month, regardless of the frequency of use.

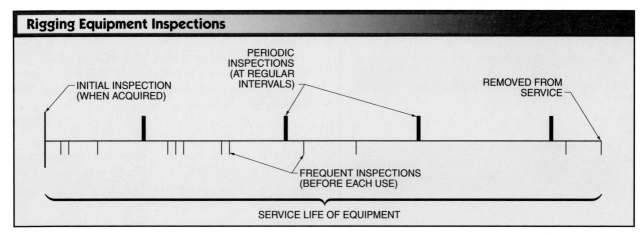

Rigging Equipment Inspections

Figure 4-2. Rigging equipment inspections include initial, periodic, and frequent inspections.

Wire Rope Inspection

After a wire rope has been in service for a short while, its breaking strength actually increases slightly. **See Figure 4-3.** The breaking strength increases because the wires settle into position within the strands, making them more solid and improving uniformity. However, further normal use decreases the strength of the wire rope, first gradually, then rapidly, due to wire breaks, corrosion, and abrasion. An ongoing inspection monitors this process so that a wire rope is removed from service before the strength decreases significantly.

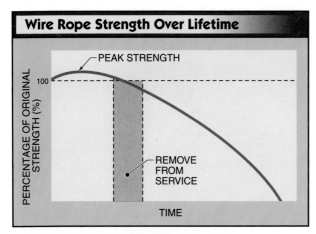

Wire Rope Strength Over Lifetime

Figure 4-3. Wire rope strengthens slightly after use, then begins to lose strength. It should be removed from service before it is significantly weakened.

Broken wires are a common problem. **See Figure 4-4.** Damage in a small area indicates physical contact with sharp edges. Wires broken in many places throughout the rope indicate a severe overloading condition. Ropes can tolerate small numbers of broken wires, but excessive numbers of breaks require that rope be removed from service. This threshold may vary depending on the rope size and type. However, a rope with a break in an entire strand must be removed immediately.

Corrosion may be general or localized. Signs of corrosion include discolored wires, rusty residue, roughened or pitted surface, or slackness within strands. A loss of diameter, often caused by corrosion, of more than 10% is considered reason for removal from service.

Kinking is a sharp bend that permanently deforms the lay of rope strands. Kinking is caused by the tightening of a loop that is restrained from untwisting. This can happen from improper storage or improper removal of wire rope from a spool. Kinking significantly weakens a wire rope.

Wire rope can be crushed when trapped under or between heavy loads. The impact distorts the arrangement of the wires in the strands and the strands in the rope. It can also break individual wires. Any sign of crushing requires removal of the rope from service.

Excessive wear on a wire rope flattens the outer layer of wires. Wear is quantified by periodically measuring the rope diameter. Rope should be replaced when the diameter reduction exceeds the allowable tolerance.

Bird caging is a type of damage to wire rope where the outer strands separate and open. This is caused when the outer layer of strands becomes longer than an inner layer. Bird caging occurs from tight pulleys, shock loading, incorrect fitting installation or swivel use, or the application of a heavy load before the strands have settled.

Loose outer wires can form small loops, often in multiple strands along one side of the rope. If rope use continues, the loops can become flattened into small tangles of wires. This deformation is often caused by shock loading, tight bends, or kinks.

Wire Rope Inspection

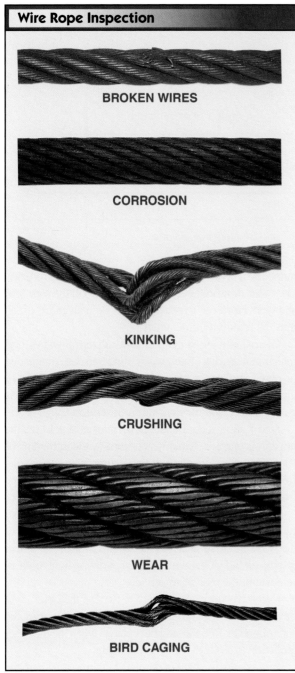

Lift-All Company, Inc.

Figure 4-4. Examples of localized wire rope damage include kinking, loose wires, and bird caging.

Core protrusion occurs when strands are forced apart and the core material is squeezed out from between the strands. This can be caused by shock loading or, in the case of fiber cores, swelling due to the absorption of moisture. This condition is also called a node, due to the localized increase in rope diameter.

Fiber Rope Inspection

Due to its more flexible nature, fiber rope can be inspected more thoroughly than wire rope. The strands of fiber rope can often be pulled open slightly to inspect the interior for dirt and grit, which can gradually wear fibers to the breaking point. Opening a rope must be done very carefully to avoid causing distortions that reduce the strength of the rope. Mold or mildew may be present in a rope that is repeatedly exposed to moisture and not dried promptly. This does not affect the strength of synthetic fiber ropes but can seriously weaken natural fiber ropes.

An exterior inspection should be done to check for signs of excessive abrasion, wear, cuts, kinks, thermal damage, or chemical damage. **See Figure 4-5.** A fiber rope under gradual abrasion and wear has many frayed surface fibers appearing like fuzz. Wear due to frequent pulley use may cause matted or glazed fibers on the surface due to heat buildup. The level of wear considered excessive depends on the extent of the damage and the proportion of the outer strands that are worn away.

Fiber Rope Inspection

Figure 4-5. Common types of damage to fiber rope include cuts, kinking, excessive wear, and thermal damage.

Cuts are localized damage caused by contact with sharp edges of loads or other equipment. Cuts with more than a few broken fibers require that the rope be removed from service. If the damage is near an end and the rope is otherwise acceptable, it may be possible to remove the damaged area with a new, clean cut and restore the shortened rope to usable capacity.

Kinks are often formed when loops of rope cannot untwist when pulled tight, distorting the lay of strands in the rope at one spot. Similar distortions can also be caused by excessively twisting the rope in either direction. Minor kinks can sometimes be undone by applying opposite twist to the rope until the rope lays flat and the strands twist uniformly. If this is not possible, the rope should be discarded. Braided and plaited ropes do not usually form kinks.

Thermal damage can be caused by excessive friction when wound around pulleys or from direct contact with flames or hot equipment. Natural fibers tend to become charred from heat, while synthetic fibers tend to melt. Very small amounts of heat damage may be acceptable, but if in doubt, the rope should be discarded.

Chemical damage may cause discoloration or physical damage to fibers. Discoloration may not affect the strength at all, but physical damage to fibers can significantly weaken rope. The degree of damage depends greatly on the chemical and type of rope fiber. Unless the exact nature of the chemical exposure is known and it is unlikely the rope was affected, then any evidence of chemical exposure is reason for removing the rope from service.

Web Sling and Round Sling Inspection

Web and round slings must include an identification tag that includes the manufacturer's name or mark, manufacturer's code or stock number, working load limits for the types of hitches permitted, and type of webbing material. **See Figure 4-6.** Use over time can obscure the printing or cause the tag to fall off, so the first part of an inspection is to check for this tag. If a tag is damaged but the sling appears otherwise acceptable, the sling may be returned to the manufacturer for testing and retagging.

Web-Sling Identification Tags

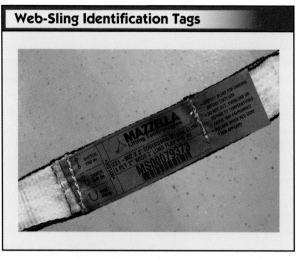

Figure 4-6. An identification tag includes the manufacturer's name or mark, manufacturer's code or stock number, working load limits for the types of hitches permitted, and type of webbing material.

Web slings include red warning yarns within the interior weave that are normally not visible. These are designed to show through if the webbing is damaged sufficiently to render it unfit for use. **See Figure 4-7.** The sling must be immediately removed from service if there is any sign of the warning yarns. However, lack of visible warning yarns does not indicate an acceptable sling condition. Some damage may not expose these yarns but can still weaken the sling. Round slings may not include any warning yarns, but the slings must be discarded if any of the interior load-bearing yarns are visible.

Web-Sling Warning Yarns

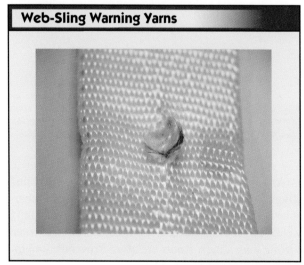

Lift-All Company, Inc.

Figure 4-7. If the red warning yarns from webbing cores are visible, then the web sling has been overloaded or damaged and must be removed from service.

Further inspection of the sling should be done to check for physical, thermal, or chemical damage that can weaken the sling. **See Figure 4-8.** Excessive wear or abrasion can damage the stitching in the load-bearing splices or cause the surface fibers to fray and break. Significant cuts or tears are those that damage 50% of the longitudinal yarns in an area that extends ¼ of the webbing width or 100% of the yarns for ⅛ of the width. Edge cuts can be particularly weakening. Other types of physical damage include punctures, snags, or embedded particles.

Thermal damage, which can be caused by direct exposure to heat or from friction, is indicated by melting or charring of the webbing material. Exposure to certain chemicals can cause disintegration of the webbing fibers, depending on the fiber material.

Lift-All Company, Inc.
Knots are a significant potential problem for web and round slings. Untie knots only if they have not yet been pulled tight under load. If a knot has been pulled tight, the strength of the sling may have been permanently compromised.

Another serious problem with both web and round slings is knots. A knot alters the load-bearing characteristics of the yarns at that location, significantly weakening the sling. Knots are easily introduced when sorting long slings. Knots are often irreversibly tightened if not caught before the sling is loaded. A sling with any knot that has been tightened under load must be removed from service.

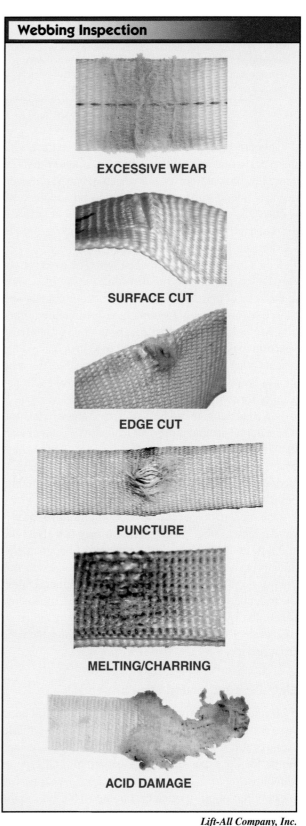

Webbing Inspection

EXCESSIVE WEAR

SURFACE CUT

EDGE CUT

PUNCTURE

MELTING/CHARRING

ACID DAMAGE

Lift-All Company, Inc.

Figure 4-8. Web and round slings are weakened by many types of physical, thermal, and chemical damage.

Chain Inspection

Rope and webbing are composed of many load-bearing elements in parallel, each providing some of the strength capacity. These materials can tolerate a certain degree of failure from some of the elements and still provide significant strength capacity. However, chain relies on load-bearing elements that are arranged in series. The failure of any single link in a chain causes the complete failure of the entire chain. Therefore, inspection of chain requires that each link be examined for structural defects. **See Figure 4-9.**

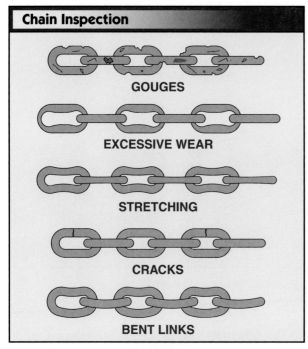

Chain Inspection

GOUGES

EXCESSIVE WEAR

STRETCHING

CRACKS

BENT LINKS

Figure 4-9. Signs of chain damage include gouges, wear, stretching, cracks, and distorted links.

The chain must be cleaned of all dirt and grease, which can hide some signs of damage. Each link should be inspected for cuts, gouges, and nicks, which can eventually lead to cracks that cause link breakage. Repeated flexing and loading can cause links to become thinner at their contact points. This area should be measured and compared to the minimum allowable diameter for the chain size. **See Figure 4-10.**

Overloading a chain causes a gradual stretching of the links, giving them a resemblance to a figure eight. Chain is designed to elongate in this manner before breaking, providing a visual indication that the chain must be replaced. Links should also not be bent from their usual shape, which hinders their ability to seat and flex properly.

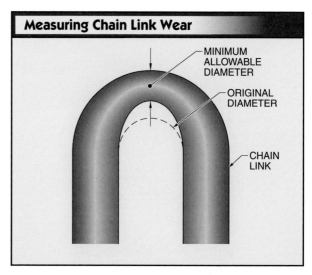

Measuring Chain Link Wear

MINIMUM ALLOWABLE DIAMETER

ORIGINAL DIAMETER

CHAIN LINK

Figure 4-10. The contact points in chain links gradually wear and thin but may remain in service if it meets a specified minimum diameter.

Attachment Inspection

The variety of attachments, hardware, and fittings used when rigging and lifting must also be inspected. Like chain, these metal components must be cleaned and individually inspected. Signs of damage include cuts, gouges, cracks, breaks, corrosion, and pitting. Overloading causes distortions such as elongation, twisting, and opening (for hooks).

RIGGING EQUIPMENT STORAGE

Proper care, use, and storage of rigging equipment prevents damage and ensures safety. Rigging equipment should be kept in a designated and organized area that is kept clean, dry, and away from harmful fumes or heat. All wet equipment must be hung up in fresh, circulating air to speed the drying process before storage. Synthetic webbing, round slings, and natural fiber rope are vulnerable to degradation from ultraviolet light, so they should be stored out of sunlight and away from areas used for arc welding.

Rope should be stored on spools or rolled into coils. Coiling rope usually requires twisting as it is looped, so that it lies flat. When uncoiling, the rope must be untwisted. **See Figure 4-11.** Pulling on the rope without untwisting it can cause kinking if the loops are drawn tight. Alternatively, coiling the rope into a figure eight avoids the need to twist the rope and makes uncoiling easier. Figure-eight coils may require more storage hooks to keep the loops from tangling.

Coiling Rope

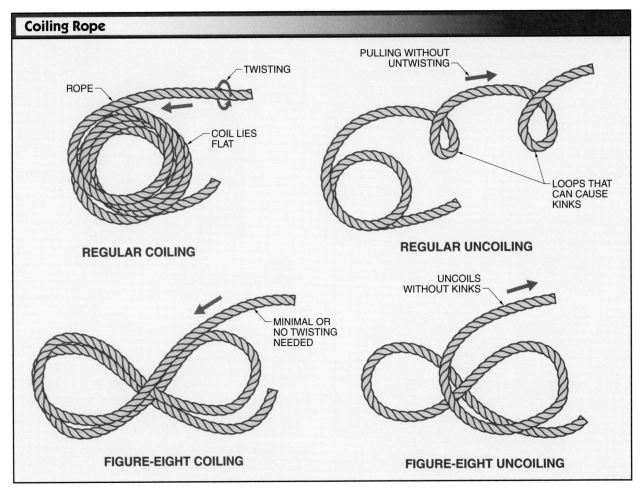

Figure 4-11. The method of coiling rope affects how easy it is to uncoil without causing kinks.

Web and round slings should be neatly hung from racks, preferably vertically. They should be wiped clean to remove as much dirt and abrasive grit as possible. Slings or sling components must not be left where vehicles or forklifts may run over them or where heavy loads may be set on them. Avoid dragging slings over abrasive surfaces or sharp objects.

RIGGING EQUIPMENT RECORDKEEPING

Written records of the use and inspection of slings and other rigging equipment should be created for each new sling. A serial number is issued to each component, which is used to identify it on each of its inspection records. The extent of inspection records and frequency of inspections may vary depending on the applicable requirements and the amount of rigging done by the user. The inspection records should be kept neat and organized.

The minimum recommended information on an inspection document includes the serial number, manufacturer, size, rated capacity, attachments, condition notations for each component, and whether the component must be removed from service. **See Figure 4-12.** Information on the inspection typically includes the date, department, inspection type, rigging type, and inspector name. Records for frequent inspections may also include the dates, hours, and locations of each use, along with the lifting conditions.

> ⚡ **Factoid**
>
> Rigging equipment and associated purchasing and inspection records must be kept in a clean and organized location. A preferable location is in a room that is near, but separate from, the main work area. Hooks and other storage organizers should be provided to properly arrange slings and accessories.

Rigging Inspection Record

Rigging Inspection

Date ___Jan. 14th___   Department ___Shipping___

Inspector ___J. Smith___   Inspection Type ___Monthly___

Rigging: Wire Rope / Fiber Rope / (Web Slings)/ Round Slings / Chain / Other _____

Serial Number	Manufacturer	Size	Rated Capacity	Attachments	Condition	Removed from Service?
W-010	NB Slings	6″	9600	triangles	Good	N
W-029	NB Slings	4″	6400	none	½″ edge tear	YES—destroyed
W-007	Lift-Tech	6″	16,800	choker/triangle	light wear	N
W-013	Lift-Tech	8″	19,200	none	unreadable tag	YES—returned to mfr.

Figure 4-12. The collection of inspection records for a particular piece of equipment offers enough historical information to chart equipment degradation and life expectancy.

5

Lifting Devices

Lifting devices use the principle of mechanical advantage to lift loads. This allows very heavy loads to be lifted with far less force, although it is at the expense of speed. Mechanical advantage is accomplished through block and tackle, the drive systems of hoists, or both used together to multiply the advantage. Several types of hoists are used in industrial applications, including those with manual, electrical, and pneumatic power sources. Many hoists include common mechanisms and safety features that must be inspected thoroughly before use to ensure proper operation.

Objectives

- Describe how block and tackle provides mechanical advantage.
- Compare the effects of mechanical advantage on force, travel, and speed.
- Differentiate between the lead-line forces needed to hold and lift a load.
- Determine the loading on blocks due to various tackle assemblies.
- Compare the operation and applications of various types of hoists.
- Describe the considerations for properly wrapping rope on a hoist drum.
- Detail the inspections and tests required for safe hoist operations.

BLOCK AND TACKLE

Many lifting devices in use today use the centuries-old principle of block and tackle. Block and tackle were used to move sails, spars, and other components on sailing ships. Much of the block and tackle terminology used today is based on nautical applications, though most modern block and tackle is primarily used for industrial lifting.

A *block* is an assembly of one or more pulleys in a frame. **See Figure 5-1.** *Tackle* is the combination of ropes and accessories arranged with blocks to gain mechanical advantage for lifting. Block and tackle assemblies begin with the rope being attached at one point and reeved over one or more pulleys. *Reeving* is the passing of a rope through an opening or around a pulley. Rope can be reeved over multiple pulleys in succession to increase mechanical advantage.

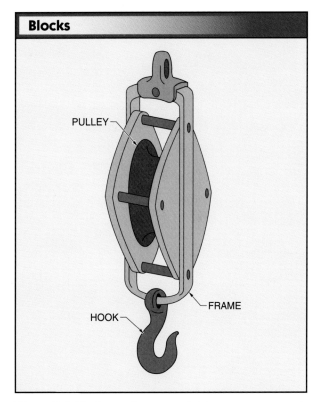

Figure 5-1. Blocks are frames containing one or more pulleys that are used in block and tackle assemblies.

Mechanical Advantage

Mechanical advantage is the ratio of the output force from a machine to the input force applied. In block and tackle applications, a mechanical advantage means that a load can be lifted by applying a force less than the load weight. The tradeoff is that the lifting is slower and requires longer rope.

The mechanical advantage of block and tackle is determined by its number of parts. **See Figure 5-2.** A *part* is a rope length between a hook and block or between two blocks. One-part reeving has one line between the load and a single block. The lead line is not counted as a part. A *lead line* is the part of the rope to which force is applied to hold or move a load. There is no mechanical advantage to one-part reeving. The force required to lift the load is equal to the weight of the load.

Two-part reeving has two lengths of rope between lower and upper blocks. The rope is attached to the upper block, reeved through the lower block, reeved through the upper block, and then becomes the lead line. The weight of the lower block must also be considered as part of the load weight, but this is usually an insignificant addition. Two-part reeving has a mechanical advantage of 2:1, reducing the lead-line force to only 50%.

A three-part reeving involves two pulleys in an upper block and one in a lower block. This arrangement has three parts between the load and upper block, providing a mechanical advantage of 3:1. Each part supports ⅓ of the load, so the force on the lead line is 33% of the load weight. Block and tackle can be arranged with four or more parts for greater mechanical advantages.

The Crosby Group, Inc.
Blocks are pulley assemblies that are used in many rigging and lifting applications.

Mechanical Advantage

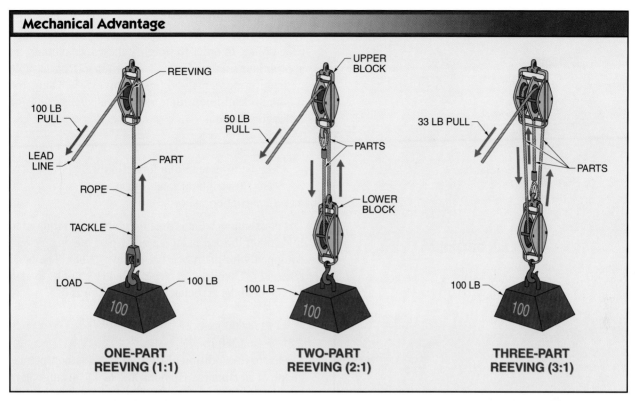

Figure 5-2. The wrapping of rope back and forth around multiple pulleys provides a mechanical advantage. Less force is required to lift a certain load.

Static Forces

A force applied to the lead line is useful only when it is equal to or greater than the static (holding) force. A static force is great enough to hold a load stationary but not lift the load. The amount of static force required to hold a load is calculated with the following formula:

$$F_S = \frac{W_{total}}{n}$$

where

F_S = static lead-line force (in lb)

W_{total} = total load weight, including rigging equipment (in lb)

n = number of parts

For example, what is the force required to hold a 500 lb load using a four-part reeving system? *Note:* The rope, block, and hook components total 30 lb.

$$F_S = \frac{W_{total}}{n}$$

$$F_S = \frac{530}{4}$$

$$F_S = \textbf{133 lb}$$

Lifting Forces

As a lead-line force exceeds the minimum static force it overcomes friction in the pulleys and the load begins to rise. The amount of additional force needed to begin lifting differs according to the number of pulleys, their bend ratio, and their bearing type. Each pulley adds friction to the system, which adds a practical limitation to the temptation of increasing the number of pulleys to a tackle arrangement for greater mechanical advantage.

Each pulley used has friction that must be overcome. Therefore, the number of pulleys affects the minimum lifting force. The number of pulleys is assumed to equal the number of parts. Bend ratio is a factor because a rope moves more easily over a larger pulley than a smaller one. The pulley bearing types have different friction characteristics. **See Figure 5-3.** The axles of plain bearing pulleys are just pins held in the frame of the block. Alternatively, ball- or roller-bearing blocks hold pulley axles in reduced-friction bearings. Less additional force is required to overcome the friction of rolling bearing pulleys than plain bearing pulleys.

Pulley Bearings

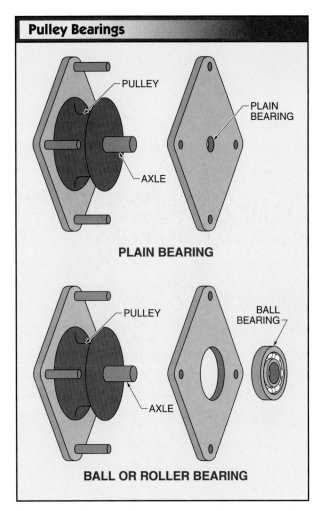

Figure 5-3. The type of bearing holding the axle of a pulley affects the amount of friction in the pulley.

Friction in each pulley adds a certain percentage of the load's weight as resistance. **See Figure 5-4.** Plain bearing pulleys typically add 5% to 8%. Ball- or roller-bearing pulleys typically add 3% to 5%. For example, a pulley adding 6% in friction requires a 106 lb force to move a 100 lb load using one-part reeving.

Pulley Friction Contributions

Bend Ratio	Plain Bearing	Ball or Roller Bearing
up to 15	8%	5%
15 to 20	7%	4%
greater than 20	6%	3%

Figure 5-4. The amount of friction resistance produced by a pulley when lifting depends on the bend ratio and type of pulley bearing.

For multiple-part reeving, the load is shared by each part, but the effect of friction compounds through each pulley. In order to simplify these calculations, an appropriate friction factor is determined from a table of friction percentages. **See Figure 5-5.** Then, the minimum lead-line lifting force is calculated with the following formula:

$$F_L = W_{total} \times f_{fr}$$

where

F_L = lifting lead-line force (in lb)

W_{total} = weight of load (in lb)

f_{fr} = friction factor

For example, what is the minimum force required to lift a 6000 lb load using an eight-part reeving system equipped with plain bearing pulleys? *Note:* The bend ratio is 17. Therefore, each pulley adds 7% of its load in friction and the associated friction factor is 0.21.

$$F_L = W_{total} \times f_{fr}$$
$$F_L = 6000 \times 0.21$$
$$F_L = \textbf{1260 lb}$$

Due to the addition of friction factors, the true mechanical advantage of a block and tackle arrangement when lifting is less than the same arrangement when static. For example, to hold a 6000 lb load steady with an eight-part reeving system, the mechanical advantage is 8:1. The static lead-line force is only 750 lb. However, to lift the load, a minimum force of 1260 lb is required to overcome friction. The true mechanical advantage in this case is approximately 4.8:1 (6000 lb ÷ 1260 lb = 4.8).

Harrington Hoists, Inc.
Some hoists include integrated block and tackle, which increases the hoist's mechanical advantage.

Pulley Friction Factors

Number of Parts	Pulley Friction Contribution					
	3%	4%	5%	6%	7%	8%
1	1.03	1.04	1.05	1.06	1.07	1.08
2	0.53	0.54	0.55	0.56	0.57	0.58
3	0.36	0.37	0.39	0.40	0.41	0.42
4	0.28	0.29	0.30	0.32	0.33	0.34
5	0.23	0.24	0.26	0.27	0.28	0.29
6	0.20	0.21	0.22	0.24	0.25	0.26
7	0.18	0.19	0.20	0.21	0.23	0.24
8	0.16	0.17	0.18	0.20	0.21	0.23
9	0.14	0.16	0.17	0.19	0.20	0.22
10	0.13	0.15	0.16	0.18	0.20	0.22
11	0.13	0.14	0.16	0.17	0.19	0.21
12	0.12	0.13	0.15	0.17	0.19	0.21

Figure 5-5. Pulley friction factors are used to calculate the lead-line force required to overcome pulley friction and lift a load.

Travel Distance and Speed

A block and tackle arrangement amplifies force at the cost of distance. As more pulleys reduce the force required to lift a load, the distance the lead line must be pulled increases. The proportions are equal to the static mechanical advantage. **See Figure 5-6.** For example, if a two-part reeve is used to lift a load by 12″, the lead line must be pulled 24″. If the tackle is a three-part reeving, then the load would lift by only 8″.

Travel speed is affected in the same manner as travel distance. If the two lines are traveling different distances in the same amount of time, the speeds are also different. If the lead line travels 24″ in the same amount of time that the load travels 12″, then the load's lifting speed is ½ of the lead line's speed. Similarly, a three-part reeved load moves at one-third the speed of the lead line. In a block and tackle assembly, no two pulleys travel at the same speed.

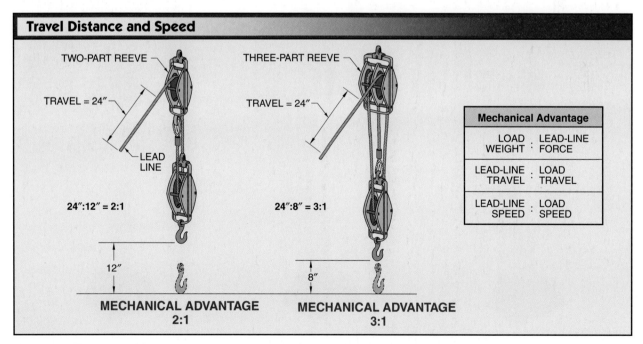

Figure 5-6. The reduced force requirements due to mechanical advantage are at the expense of line travel and speed. For a particular load being lifted a certain distance, the lead-line force is less, the travel is more, and the speed is greater.

Block Loading Forces

In addition to determining the lifting and pulling forces, the working load limit of a block must be considered. Due to the arrangement of forces in tackle assemblies, the forces on blocks can exceed the load weight significantly. The blocks must be rated to withstand the total forces they may experience.

In a simple, single-part reeving assembly, the lead-line force is equal to the load weight. **See Figure 5-7.** If the lead line is held vertical, the block experiences two forces, both equal to the load weight. Therefore, the resulting block loading force is equal to twice the load weight.

If the lead line is at an angle to the tackle assembly, the loading on the block is reduced. A block loading factor is based on the angle between the lines. **See Figure 5-8.** The resulting block loading force is calculated using the following formula:

$$F_{BL} = F_{LL} \times f_{BL}$$
where
F_{BL} = block loading force (in lb)
F_{LL} = lead-line force (in lb)
f_{BL} = block loading angle factor

For example, a 100 lb load is held static with a single-part reeving. What is the block loading force if the lead line is held at 45° to the load line?

$$F_{BL} = F_{LL} \times f_{BL}$$
$$F_{BL} = 100 \times 1.84$$
$$F_{BL} = \textbf{184 lb}$$

This formula applies to multiple-part reeving assemblies also. The force on the lead line is used in the calculation and added to the forces on the remaining parts (not counting the part that makes the angle with the lead line). For example, a 100 lb load is held static with a two-part reeving assembly where the load line is held at 45°. What is the block loading force? The static force on the lead line and each part is 50 lb. Therefore, the total force on the block is 142 lb (50 lb + [50 lb × 1.84] = 142 lb).

⚡ Factoid

Pulleys are also known as sheaves in many contexts. Therefore, some block information may refer to sheave friction. If friction information is not available, some calculations recommend adding 10% of the load as friction to provide a wider margin of safety.

Block Loading Forces

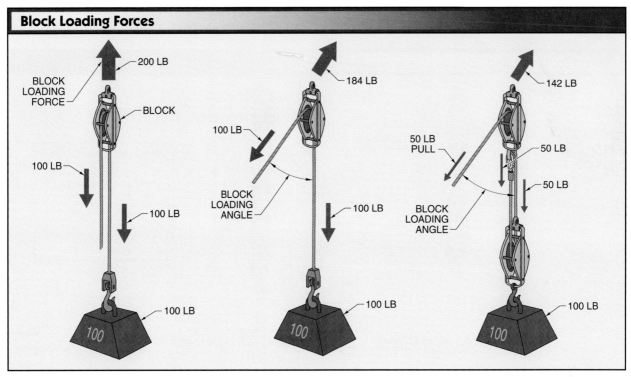

Figure 5-7. The resulting force on a block is determined from the effects of forces on each part. The block loading can be much greater than the load weight.

Block Loading Angle Factors

Angle*	Block Loading Factor
0	2.00
10	1.99
20	1.97
30	1.93
40	1.87
45	1.84
50	1.81
60	1.73
70	1.64
80	1.53
90	1.41
100	1.29
110	1.15
120	1.00
130	0.84
135	0.76
140	0.68
150	0.52
160	0.35
170	0.17

* in °

Figure 5-8. The angle at which the lead line and tackle parts go through a block affects the loading on the block, which is calculated with a block loading angle factor.

HOISTS

A *hoist* is a mechanical device used to provide the lifting force on lead lines. Hoists typically use gear drives to provide increased load capacity and safety over manual pulling. Another type of mechanical advantage gear drives provide is that a small input torque is amplified into a large output torque. *Torque* is rotational force. The output torque winds a lead line onto a drum or across a sprocket to provide the linear pulling force that lifts the load. The mechanical advantage in torque is provided at the expense of speed.

Most hoists use worm gear or bevel gear drives. **See Figure 5-9.** A *worm gear drive* is a pair of gears consisting of a spiral-threaded worm (drive gear) and a worm wheel (driven gear). The worm gear must rotate many times in order to turn the worm wheel once, which provides a very high mechanical advantage. Also, the design prevents reverse rotation of the gears, so when the input torque is removed the gears cannot slip in reverse.

A *bevel gear drive* is a pair of gears that mesh at an angle, usually 90°. The mechanical advantage of the

drive depends on the relative sizes of the gears. A small gear driving a large gear provides a large advantage, while a pair of same-sized gears provides no advantage. Unlike the worm gear hoist, bevel gear hoists normally require a braking or locking mechanism to prevent reverse rotation.

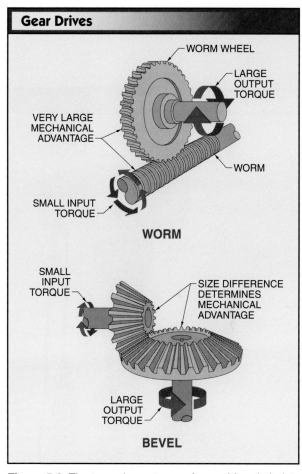

Gear Drives

Figure 5-9. The two primary types of gear drives in hoists are worm gear drives and bevel gear drives.

Hoists are suspended overhead from a top hook or another type of attachment to a supporting structure. A support may be a fixed point on a building ceiling or structure or a movable point such as a trolley or crane. The attachment and the supporting structure must be strong enough to support the weight of the hoist, tackle, rigging, and the maximum load capable of being lifted with the equipment, given the appropriate safety factor.

Hoists are specified by their capacity rating and certain critical dimensions. **See Figure 5-10.** *Lift* is the distance between a hoist's upper and lower limits of travel. *Headroom* is the distance from the cup of a hoist's top hook to the cup of the hoist hook when the hoist hook is at its upper limit of travel. This dimension specifies how much space must be allowed under the support for the hoist. *Reach* is the distance between the cup of the top hook and the cup of the hoist hook when the hoist hook is at its lower limit of travel. Reach is the sum of the lift and the headroom.

Hand-Chain Hoists. A *hand-chain hoist* is a manually operated hoist that uses a continuous hand chain to provide the input torque to the gear drive. **See Figure 5-11.** The operator rotates the hand chain, which wraps around a pocket wheel in the hoist. A *pocket wheel* is a sprocket-like wheel with chain-link pockets. The links in the hand chain engage with the pocket wheel and cause it to rotate. This operates the gear drive, which raises or lowers the load. Hand-chain hoists are normally rated for ¼ t to 50 t.

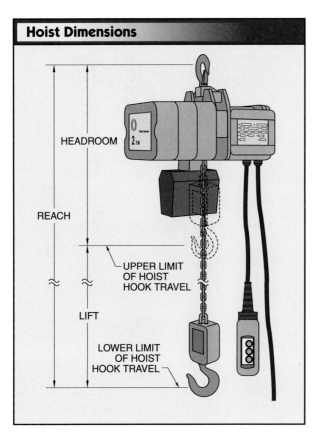

Figure 5-10. Hoists are selected based on their capacity rating and certain critical dimensions.

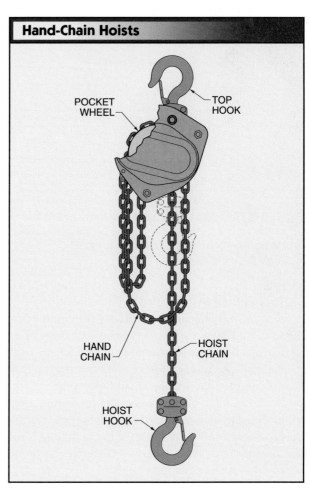

Figure 5-11. The input torque is provided to a hand-chain hoist by pulling on the continuous hand chain.

Manually Operated Hoists

A *manually operated hoist* is a hoist that provides mechanical advantage and safety features but relies on a manual force to provide the input torque. These hoists provide some means for a person to easily apply force to the hoist, such as a chain or lever. The lifting line is commonly chain.

Lever-Operated Hoists. A *lever-operated hoist* is a manually operated hoist that uses the movement of a lever to provide the input torque to the gear drive. **See Figure 5-12.** Lever-operated hoists are very compact, enabling them to be used in confined areas. Lever-operated hoists are generally limited to lightweight loads of about 500 lb or less.

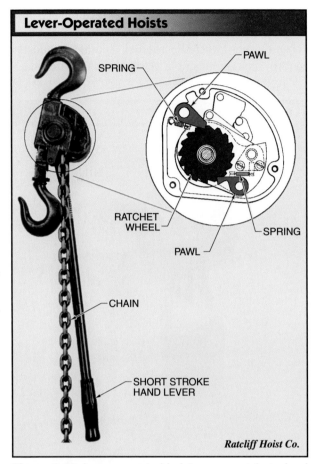

Lever-Operated Hoists

SPRING

PAWL

RATCHET WHEEL

SPRING

PAWL

CHAIN

SHORT STROKE HAND LEVER

Ratcliff Hoist Co.

Figure 5-12. Lever-operated hoists use a ratchet wheel to convert the back-and-forth motion of a lever to high output torque.

Two major types of lever-operated hoists use either ratchet or slip-clutch mechanisms. Ratchet mechanisms prevent reverse operation. A *ratchet* is a mechanism in which a toothed wheel is prevented from turning backwards by engagement with a spring-loaded pawl. A *slip clutch* is a spring-loaded, friction-held fiber disc that is adjusted to slip at 125% to 150% of the hoist's rated load. Many slip clutches are preset by the manufacturer, while others are adjustable. Adjustable slip clutches must never be adjusted to hold more than 175% of the hoist's rated load. Slip clutches are subject to failure from sudden loading, also known as shock loading. Even if the load is not excessive, a shock can cause the friction brakes to slip or freeze. For this reason, slip clutch hoists are less common.

Power-Operated Hoists

A *power-operated hoist* is a hoist operated by a power source that is controlled by an operator. The most common power sources used by hoists are electric and pneumatic power. Power-operated hoists may use either chain or wire rope as the lifting component.

All power-operated hoists are equipped with an upper limit switch as a safety mechanism to prevent damage. A *limit switch* is a device that activates when a moving component reaches the normal end of travel. The limit switch de-energizes the hoist when the hoist hook reaches the upper limit of travel. **See Figure 5-13.** Limit switches are safety switches and are not to be used as stop switches.

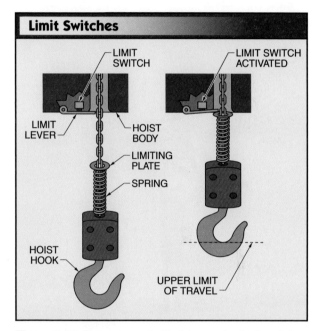

Limit Switches

LIMIT SWITCH

LIMIT SWITCH ACTIVATED

LIMIT LEVER

HOIST BODY

LIMITING PLATE

SPRING

HOIST HOOK

UPPER LIMIT OF TRAVEL

Figure 5-13. Power-operated hoists require limit switches to automatically stop the hoist when the hoist hook reaches its upper limit of travel.

Harrington Hoists, Inc.
Hoists can be installed onto trolleys that can travel along beams, providing the ability to move loads laterally.

Electric Hoists. An *electric hoist* is a power-operated hoist that includes an electric motor to provide the input torque to the gear drive. **See Figure 5-14.** Common industrial electric hoist capacities range from ¼ t to 20 t, with power supply requirements between 120 VAC and 575 VAC. Mechanical slip clutches provide protection by refusing to lift (by slipping) when a load is applied beyond the hoist's capacity. Also, brake mechanisms are activated if power is removed or lost.

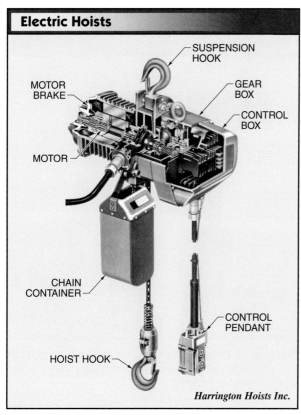

Electric Hoists

SUSPENSION HOOK

MOTOR BRAKE

GEAR BOX

CONTROL BOX

MOTOR

CHAIN CONTAINER

CONTROL PENDANT

HOIST HOOK

Harrington Hoists Inc.

Figure 5-14. An electric hoist uses an electric motor to provide the input torque to the hoist's gear drive.

An operator uses a pendant to control load movement from below. A *pendant* is a pushbutton or lever control suspended from a hoist or crane. These controls are low-voltage (normally 24 V) to provide isolation from the high operating voltage.

Pneumatic Hoists. A *pneumatic hoist* is a power-operated hoist that uses an air motor to provide the input torque to the gear drive. **See Figure 5-15.** Air motors are able to start, stop, reverse, and operate at variable speeds, all with smooth transitions. They are also inherently self-cooling, making them ideal for applications in high-temperature surroundings. Pneumatic hoists also have a distinct advantage over electric hoists when used for applications where electric arcing poses an explosion hazard, such as in paint or petrochemical facilities.

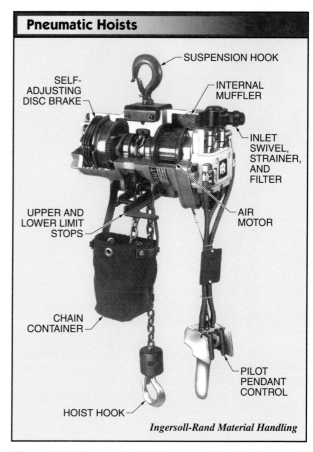

Pneumatic Hoists

SUSPENSION HOOK

SELF-ADJUSTING DISC BRAKE

INTERNAL MUFFLER

INLET SWIVEL, STRAINER, AND FILTER

UPPER AND LOWER LIMIT STOPS

AIR MOTOR

CHAIN CONTAINER

PILOT PENDANT CONTROL

HOIST HOOK

Ingersoll-Rand Material Handling

Figure 5-15. Pneumatic hoists use an air motor to convert airflow and pressure from a compressed air supply into input torque.

The compressed air supply must be sized to provide adequate airflow and pressure for the hoist capacity. Pneumatic equipment requires a certain standard cubic feet per minute (SCFM) for operation. Air compressor SCFM specifications are compared to minimum pneumatic hoist requirements to select the appropriate compressor. **See Figure 5-16.**

⚡ Factoid

Standard cubic feet per minute (SCFM) is the flow rate of a gas at "standard" conditions of temperature, pressure, and relative humidity. However, the conditions may vary between definitions of SCFM, so the specification should always be checked.

Pneumatic Hoist Airflow Requirements

Hoist Capacity*	Maximum Lift Speed†	Minimum Airflow‡	Minimum Compressor Power**
½	50	48	12
2	30	75	19
8	20	260	65
15	8	420	105

* in t
† in feet per minute (fpm), based on 90 psi line pressure
‡ in SCFM
** in horsepower (HP)

Figure 5-16. The minimum compressed air supply specifications for a hoist depend on the hoist's lifting capacity and speed.

Drum Wrap

Hoists that use rope for the hoisting line wrap the rope around a drum as the load is lifted. A *drum* is a cylinder on the output of a hoist that rope is wound onto or unwound from. Rope must be wound properly onto a drum to avoid kinking or tangling the rope.

The first layer of rope establishes the pattern for proper winding. Some drums are grooved to help keep each wrap in place. **See Figure 5-17.** Smooth drums require that the first layer of rope be wound tightly, with each wrap as close as possible to the preceding wrap. This first layer then guides the wraps in successive layers. For this reason, the entire first layer should not be unwound on a smooth drum. Even on grooved drums, there must always be a two-wrap minimum. If the drum becomes completely unwound, the attachment that binds the rope to the drum may not be strong enough to hold the load alone.

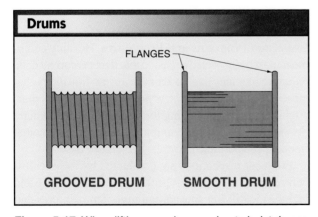

Figure 5-17. When lifting, rope is wound onto hoist drums. Some hoist drums contain grooves to guide the rope into the proper wrapping pattern.

The proper direction for winding the first layer on a drum is determined by the lay of the rope. **See Figure 5-18.** The rope lay also determines whether the rope is wound over or under on the spool. For example, the rope should be overwound from left to right if the rope is anchored on the left and the rope is a right-lay rope.

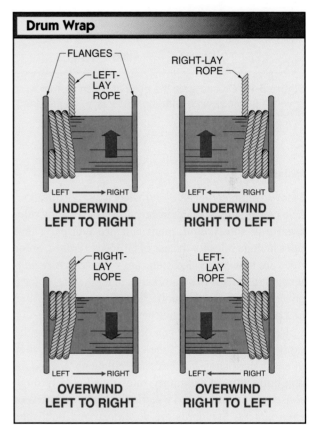

Figure 5-18. The pattern in which rope should be wound onto a drum depends on the rope lay and direction.

As the rope is forced up to the second layer at the flange, a reverse helix is created, causing the rope to cross over. **See Figure 5-19.** A *crossover* is a rope wrap winding on top of the preceding wrap. The crossover is the point at which the rope winds back over two rope grooves to advance. An undesirable condition occurs if the drum wraps enough rope that the load block comes into contact with the hoist or crane, which can severely damage the rope.

The initial winding of a hoist drum involves transferring rope from a reel. A *reel* is a wooden cylinder on which rope is wound for shipping and storage. During rope transfer, the unreeling process should be straight and under tension. Gloves should always be worn when handling wire rope.

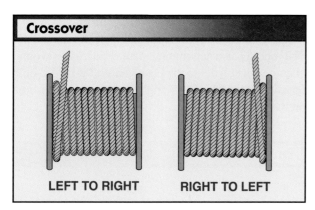

Figure 5-19. Crossover is the point at which a drum wrap covers a previous wrap, starting a new layer on the drum.

Hoist Safety

Many government agencies and independent organizations help ensure safe work environments by developing rules regarding safety equipment and procedures. These rules include rules for the use of hoists and cranes. Some rules are mandatory and some are voluntary. A *regulation* is a rule made mandatory by a federal, state, or local government. A *code* is a collection of regulations related to a particular trade or environment.

Units of government can develop their own regulations, but since this is a time-consuming process, they often adopt existing standards as regulations. A *standard* is a collection of voluntary rules developed through consensus and related to a particular trade, industry, or environment. Standards are developed and published by standards organizations, often industry-specific, that periodically review and refine the rules in the standards. Standards themselves have no authority unless they are adopted as regulations. Then they become mandatory and are enforceable by the adopting government unit.

Regulatory and standards organizations pertinent to hoist safety include the following:

- The Occupational Safety and Health Administration (OSHA) specifies safety standards through the U.S. Department of Labor and the Occupational Safety and Health Act. OSHA is concerned with the development and enforcement of safety standards for industrial workers.
- The American National Standards Institute (ANSI) is a standards-developing organization that adopts and copublishes standards that are written and approved by member organizations. ANSI manages United States participation in ISO activities.

- The International Organization for Standardization (ISO) is a nongovernmental international organization of the national standards institutions of over 150 countries. The ISO provides a worldwide forum for the standards developing process.
- The Crane Manufacturers Association of America, Inc. (CMAA) is an organization of the leading U.S. crane manufacturers that promotes standardization and proper equipment selection and use. CMAA is instrumental in establishing many crane operation standards.
- ASME International, formerly known as the American Society of Mechanical Engineers, helps establish safe structural design of hoists and cranes. ASME also develops safety standards for rigging, hoists, and cranes.
- The National Fire Protection Association (NFPA) publishes the National Electrical Code® (NFPA 70), which contains standards for the safeguarding of persons and property from hazards arising from the use of electricity. Article 610 covers the installation of electrical equipment and wiring for cranes and hoists.

Company procedures must comply with minimum federal, state, and local regulations. A company may also adopt additional rules or standards that exceed the minimum regulation requirements. These are not enforceable by law, but compliance may be a condition of employment.

✚ Safety Tip

For maximum safety for personnel, hoists and cranes should never be used to lift, support, or transport personnel unless they are specifically designed for this purpose. Loads or empty hooks should never be allowed to pass over personnel.

Inspection Programs and Procedures. Hoisting equipment must be inspected to ensure that it meets current code requirements and has no damage or modifications that present safety hazards. A new piece of equipment is thoroughly inspected according to a step-by-step procedure. **See Appendix.** Existing equipment must be inspected at frequent and periodic intervals. **See Figure 5-20.**

Frequent inspections are conducted by the operator before each use. These checks are mostly visual and include identifying unusual sounds or temperatures that may indicate problems. A checklist form is sometimes used, but it may not be necessary for the operator to fill in and file the form for long-term records.

Electric Hoist Checklist

Item	Daily	Monthly	Semi-annually	Deficiencies
All functional operating mechanisms	✓	✓	✓	Maladjustment interfering with proper operation, excessive component wear
Controls	✓		✓	Improper operation
Safety Devices	✓		✓	Malfunction
Hooks	✓	✓	✓	Deformation, chemical damage, 15% in excess of normal throat opening, 10% twist from plane of unbent hook, cracks
Load-bearing components (except rope or chain)	✓	✓	✓	Damage (especially if hook is twisted or pulling open)
Load-bearing rope	✓	✓	✓	Wear, twist, distortion, improper dead-ending, deposits of foreign material
Load-bearing chain	✓	✓	✓	Wear, twist, distortion, improper dead-ending, deposits of foreign material
Fasteners	✓	✓	✓	Not tight
Drums, pulleys, sprockets			✓	Cracks, excessive wear
Pins, bearings, shafts, gears, rollers, locking and clamping devices			✓	Cracks, excessive wear, distortion, corrosion
Brakes	✓		✓	Excessive wear, drift
Electrical			✓	Pitting, loose wires
Contactors, limit switches, pushbutton stations			✓	Deterioration, contact wear, loose wires
Hook retaining members (collars, nuts) and pins, welds, or rivets securing them			✓	Not tight or secure
Supporting structure or trolley			✓	Continued ability to support imposed loads
Warning label	✓		✓	Removed or illegible
Pushbutton markings	✓		✓	Removed or illegible
Capacity marking	✓		✓	Removed or illegible

Figure 5-20. Lifting equipment must be inspected at frequent and periodic intervals.

Periodic inspections occur either monthly or semi-annually depending on the equipment and regulations. These inspections are conducted by trained and designated personnel who examine the conditions of load-bearing components (such as hooks, wire rope, and chain) and nut and bolt tightness. Periodic inspection checklists must also cover safety features such as braking systems and limit switches. Written reports of periodic inspections are signed, dated, and placed in the equipment identification file. Inspection checklists are adapted as needed, often from checklists provided by the manufacturer.

Any repairs or major adjustments performed as a result of the inspection must be recorded on a written report. The report should identify the hoist serviced and indicate the work performed, the date, the reason for repair, the individual performing the inspection, and the parts replaced.

Hoist Brake Inspections. Braking systems must be inspected for hook drift before each shift change or prior to use after periods of nonuse. *Hook drift* is the continued travel of a hoist hook caused by insufficient motor braking. To inspect for hook drift, the hoist is operated in the lifting and lowering direction without a load on the hook. The hook is then stopped abruptly. The drift of the hook should not exceed 1″ in either direction.

Hook drift is often caused by wearing or misalignment of the disc-type friction brakes. These motor brakes are engaged by DC-powered coils. **See Figure 5-21.** The air gap in the brake assembly is set at a specific spacing (typically 0.03″) but increases as the brake lining wears. If the gap is too large, the brake will not engage. If a limit switch is added to the assembly, it will not allow the hoist motor to start if the gap reaches a worn limit.

Hoist Motor Brake Wiring Diagram

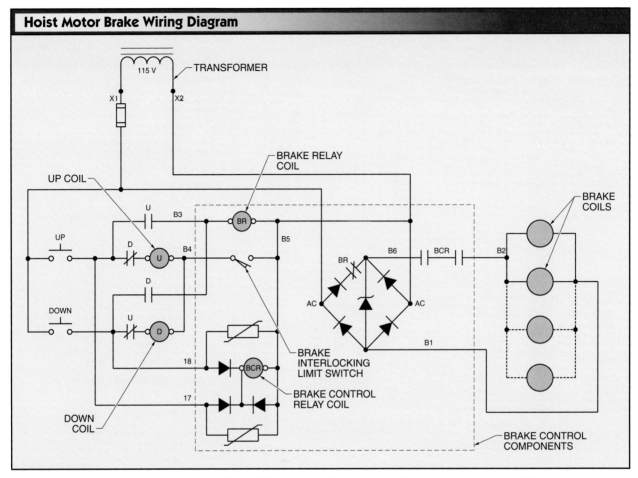

Figure 5-21. Most of the hoist motor control circuit is involved in the control of the brake mechanism. A limit switch prevents the motor from operating if activated, which occurs if the brake lining gap is excessive or misaligned.

To inspect the brake assembly, the power source is locked out and tagged out. A brush or compressed air is used to remove accumulated brake lining dust from the air gap between the coil and plates. The air gap at all three adjusting points is then checked. If the air gap is too large, the lining needs to be replaced. If it varies, the adjustment springs are weak or broken, or overheating has deformed the brake lining or compression plates. Removed brake linings are inspected for deformation by laying a straightedge across the center and checking for gaps as the straightedge is rotated. **See Figure 5-22.**

A mechanical load brake test checks the hoist braking system for proper operation when under load. All personnel should be alerted that a free-fall condition could exist during a mechanical load brake test. Warning signs and barriers must be used on the floor beneath a hoist, crane, or lifting system.

Brake Lining Inspection

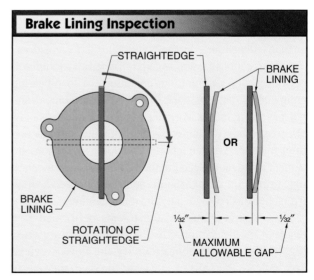

Figure 5-22. A straightedge is placed across a hoist brake lining in order to check for deformation.

During a mechanical load brake test, a load equal to the rated capacity is attached to the hoist hook and any slack in the lines is slowly taken up. The load is raised a few inches and stopped. If the load stops and the brakes hold, the load is raised and lowered several feet, stopping the hoist several times, in each direction to check the brakes. Next, the hoist is checked with a load equal to 125% of its rated load capacity. This tests any load-limiting devices, which are normally rated at 110% of the hoist's rated capacity.

Hoist Limit Switch Tests. Hoist limit switches are tested by operating an unloaded hoist in the lifting direction until the limit switch is actuated, which should immediately stop the hoist. The hoist should be inched up to the limit switch slowly. If the limit switch appears to be faulty, a continuity tester can be used to indicate open or closed circuits without the need for electrical power. After the switch has been checked or corrected, all guards and safety devices are installed and reactivated.

Cranes 6

When relatively small loads must be lifted and moved, lifting devices such as block and tackle or a hoist can usually be used. However, for large or outdoor loads the lift may require a crane. A crane includes a hoist, but also has a large structure that provides the hoist with an extended reach, both vertically and horizontally. Cranes are often used in assembly, material handling, and construction. Industrial cranes are typically indoor devices used in manufacturing or maintenance. Mobile cranes can be moved, which allows them to be relocated as they are needed.

Objectives

- Describe the qualifications and responsibilities of a crane operator.
- Detail a general lifting procedure.
- Identify the role of hand signals in performing a lift.
- Describe and differentiate between common types of industrial cranes.
- Describe and differentiate between common types of mobile cranes.
- List the common problems to be identified in a crane inspection.

CRANE OPERATION

A *crane* is a combination of a hoist with a structure to support and move a load. The operation of a crane to lift and move a load involves many different rigging and lifting principles, including weight and balance, sling hitches, capacity ratings, safety factors, proper attachment selection, and hoist operation. Cranes use many different types of mechanical advantage to be able to easily work with loads that would otherwise be very difficult or impossible to lift and move.

Cranes are broadly classified into fixed and mobile types. **See Figure 6-1.** Dozens of different fixed-crane designs are available. Each type is adapted to a specific purpose, though only a few are common in industrial settings. Fixed cranes are permanently installed and are intended for long-term use. Mobile cranes can be brought to a job site temporarily for a relatively small number of lifts.

> ⚡ **Factoid**
>
> Lifting must always be done in smooth, controlled motions. Sudden or jerky movements, rapid dropping, and high speeds can damage the load or lifting equipment. The load must always be in view of the hoist operator or an assistant giving hand signals.

Crane Operators

The crane operator is held directly responsible for the safe operation of the crane. The operator must be properly trained in rigging and lifting procedures and thoroughly familiar with the operation and features of the particular model being used. Crane operation requires skill, extreme care, good judgment, alertness, and concentration. Lifting may be performed only after the operator ensures that all rigging, hoisting, and crane components are within specifications. Crane operators must adhere to safety rules and practices as outlined in applicable and current ANSI and OSHA standards.

Individuals who cannot speak the appropriate language, read and understand printed instructions, and legally operate the equipment should not be permitted to operate a crane. Any individual who is hearing or vision impaired or may be suffering from a heart condition or other ailments that might interfere with safe performance should not operate a crane.

Depending on the size and type, cranes are operated from a cab or pendant pushbutton station. A *cab* is a compartment or platform attached to the crane from which an operator may ride. **See Figure 6-2.** A pendant hangs down from the hoists of smaller industrial cranes. This pendant includes controls for the direction and speed of the various crane motions.

Cranes

Lift-All Company, Inc.

FIXED   MOBILE

Figure 6-1. Cranes are broadly classified as either fixed (permanently installed) or mobile types.

Crane Operator Cab

Figure 6-2. Large cranes are typically operated from inside a cab, which moves with the crane to maintain a good view of the load.

Depending on the size and circumstances of the lift, the crane operator may work with other personnel to ensure that safe and proper procedures are followed. Rigging personnel are in charge of determining the appropriate rigging type, calculating weights and capacities, and selecting the proper equipment. An operator's assistant supports the crane operator in placing the lift hook and directing the load travel.

General Lifting Procedures

Exact lifting procedures vary depending on the particular circumstances, but several general rules apply. Once the hoist is brought directly over the load's center of gravity, the rigger should check that no lines or chains are twisted, overwrapped, or unseated. The rigging is connected to the hook, ensuring that the hook latch is fully closed.

The hook is raised slowly until all slack is removed. The load is then lifted slowly until it is clear of its supports and properly balanced. At this time, the operator may increase the lifting speed. When loads are lowered, the speed should be decreased gradually. Crane motions should always be smooth and gradual. Abrupt or jerky movements cause the load to swing, which can cause it to shift, put extra stress on the rigging, or impact other equipment.

Cranes are often used at construction or industrial sites that involve many people, simultaneous activities, and noisy equipment. It is imperative that all personnel at the site be alert when working around cranes and other lifting equipment. Personnel not involved in the lift must keep clear of the area around the crane and the load, its intended path of travel, and its destination.

A lift should never be attempted if the load is beyond the capacity ratings of any of the rigging, lifting, or crane components. Also, a crane should never be used to pull a load at an angle. **See Figure 6-3.** If the hoist hook cannot be positioned directly over the load lift point, either the crane or the load must be relocated.

Load Lifting

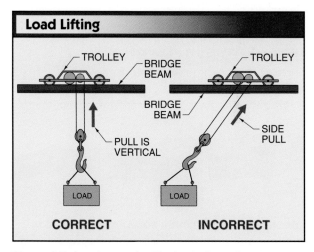

Figure 6-3. Loads must be lifted only from directly above. Side pulling is not permitted.

Hand Signals

Many cab-operated cranes require the assistance of ground personnel to ensure safe lifting and transportation of the load. In some situations, the crane operator may not have a clear view of the load being hoisted or the final position of the load. A crane operator may depend upon ground personnel to properly guide the load to its final position.

Effective communication between a crane operator and ground personnel is essential to ensure a safe lift. Two-way radios are often used for communication. However, interference due to location or other operations being performed on the job site may reduce the range and effectiveness of two-way radios.

The standard ANSI B30.5, *Mobile and Locomotive Cranes* includes a set of standard hand signals to indicate various crane operations. **See Figure 6-4.** Only an experienced and designated individual should give hand signals as the wrong signal may result in damage to materials or serious injury to individuals working near the crane. On large projects, there is often an individual specifically designated to work with the crane operator. On smaller projects, however, the signaling may be performed by a supervisor.

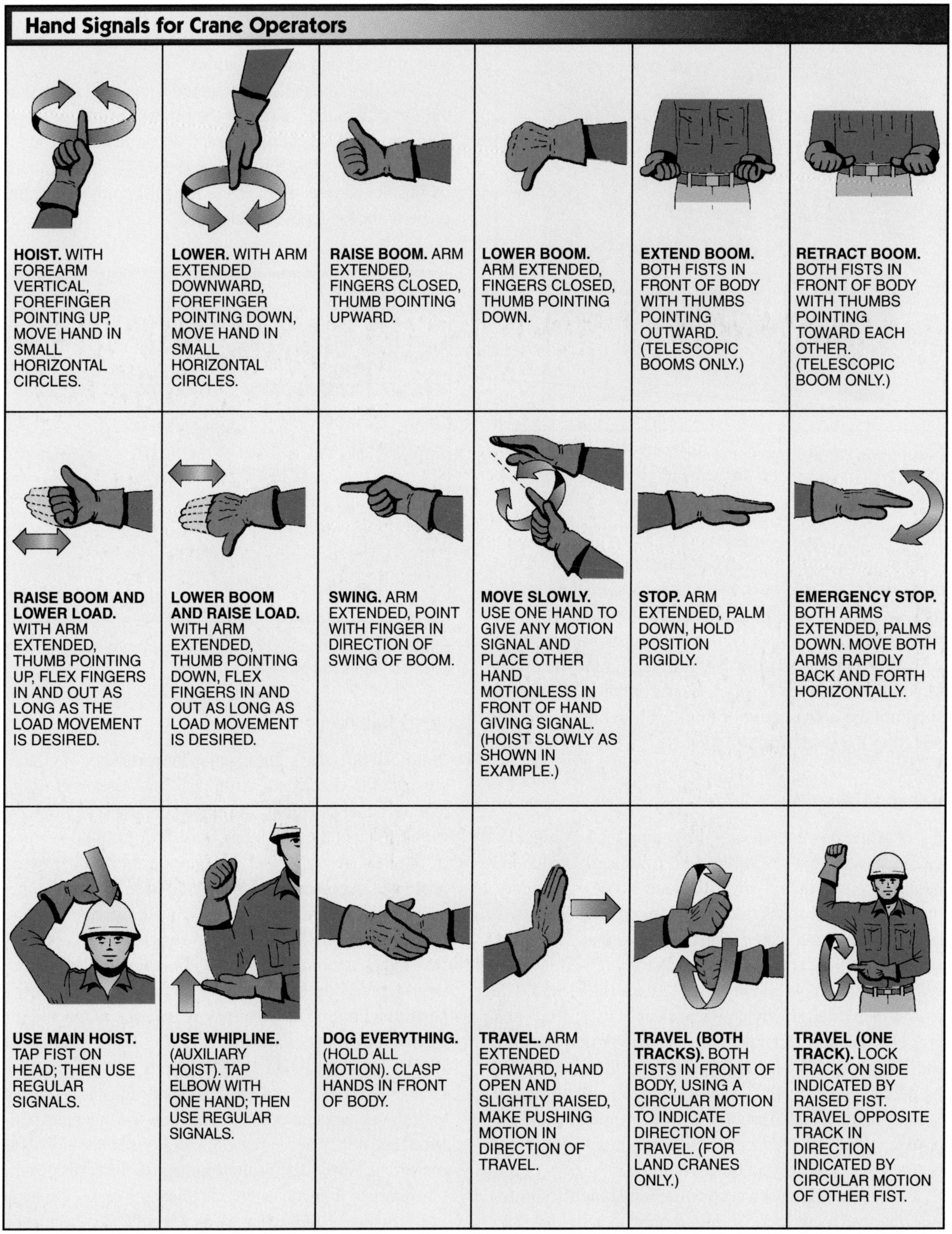

Hand Signals for Crane Operators

HOIST. WITH FOREARM VERTICAL, FOREFINGER POINTING UP, MOVE HAND IN SMALL HORIZONTAL CIRCLES.

LOWER. WITH ARM EXTENDED DOWNWARD, FOREFINGER POINTING DOWN, MOVE HAND IN SMALL HORIZONTAL CIRCLES.

RAISE BOOM. ARM EXTENDED, FINGERS CLOSED, THUMB POINTING UPWARD.

LOWER BOOM. ARM EXTENDED, FINGERS CLOSED, THUMB POINTING DOWN.

EXTEND BOOM. BOTH FISTS IN FRONT OF BODY WITH THUMBS POINTING OUTWARD. (TELESCOPIC BOOMS ONLY.)

RETRACT BOOM. BOTH FISTS IN FRONT OF BODY WITH THUMBS POINTING TOWARD EACH OTHER. (TELESCOPIC BOOM ONLY.)

RAISE BOOM AND LOWER LOAD. WITH ARM EXTENDED, THUMB POINTING UP, FLEX FINGERS IN AND OUT AS LONG AS THE LOAD MOVEMENT IS DESIRED.

LOWER BOOM AND RAISE LOAD. WITH ARM EXTENDED, THUMB POINTING DOWN, FLEX FINGERS IN AND OUT AS LONG AS LOAD MOVEMENT IS DESIRED.

SWING. ARM EXTENDED, POINT WITH FINGER IN DIRECTION OF SWING OF BOOM.

MOVE SLOWLY. USE ONE HAND TO GIVE ANY MOTION SIGNAL AND PLACE OTHER HAND MOTIONLESS IN FRONT OF HAND GIVING SIGNAL. (HOIST SLOWLY AS SHOWN IN EXAMPLE.)

STOP. ARM EXTENDED, PALM DOWN, HOLD POSITION RIGIDLY.

EMERGENCY STOP. BOTH ARMS EXTENDED, PALMS DOWN. MOVE BOTH ARMS RAPIDLY BACK AND FORTH HORIZONTALLY.

USE MAIN HOIST. TAP FIST ON HEAD; THEN USE REGULAR SIGNALS.

USE WHIPLINE. (AUXILIARY HOIST). TAP ELBOW WITH ONE HAND; THEN USE REGULAR SIGNALS.

DOG EVERYTHING. (HOLD ALL MOTION). CLASP HANDS IN FRONT OF BODY.

TRAVEL. ARM EXTENDED FORWARD, HAND OPEN AND SLIGHTLY RAISED, MAKE PUSHING MOTION IN DIRECTION OF TRAVEL.

TRAVEL (BOTH TRACKS). BOTH FISTS IN FRONT OF BODY, USING A CIRCULAR MOTION TO INDICATE DIRECTION OF TRAVEL. (FOR LAND CRANES ONLY.)

TRAVEL (ONE TRACK). LOCK TRACK ON SIDE INDICATED BY RAISED FIST. TRAVEL OPPOSITE TRACK IN DIRECTION INDICATED BY CIRCULAR MOTION OF OTHER FIST.

Figure 6-4. If a crane operator lacks a good view of the load at all times, an assistant nearby can provide crane directions through hand signals.

Loads should not be moved unless standard crane signals are clearly given, seen, and understood. The operator must pay particular attention to the required moves signaled by the assistant. The operator takes signals only from the designated assistant. The only exception to this rule is that the operator must obey a stop signal, from anyone, at all times.

INDUSTRIAL CRANES

An *industrial crane* is an indoor crane with permanent structural beam supports. Industrial cranes are typically installed indoors in a factory, warehouse, or other type of industrial space and are used to move materials and machinery. These cranes are composed of a hoist that can travel horizontally on a long beam that is supported by other structural members. Industrial cranes are generally classified based on the type and design of the supporting structural members.

Gantry Cranes

A *gantry crane* is an industrial crane composed of a bridge beam supported on legs. **See Figure 6-5.** The bridge beam is the high horizontal beam that holds the hoist. The legs may be fixed to the floor, but usually they include end trucks that allow the entire crane to travel back and forth on floor rails. An *end truck* is a roller assembly consisting of a frame, wheels, and bearings. Floor rails are small-gauge railroad rails that are recessed into, or set on top of, the floor surface. A gantry crane allows its hoist to travel in two directions, which allows it to reach any spot within a rectangular area.

A traditional gantry crane design includes two legs to support the ends of the bridge beam. These double-leg gantry cranes run on two parallel floor rails. However, if a gantry crane is to be installed along a straight wall, the design can be modified to use the wall as one of the supports. This is done by fixing a beam to the wall to serve as an overhead crane rail. This is known as a single-leg gantry crane.

Smaller, double-leg gantry cranes on regular wheels are also available. This design allows the gantry crane to be moved across any flat floor surface. These cranes can be easily pushed to where they are needed in the facility.

> ⚡ **Factoid**
> Hoist or crane operators may require certification for each type of equipment they will operate. Certification may involve both classroom instruction and field training.

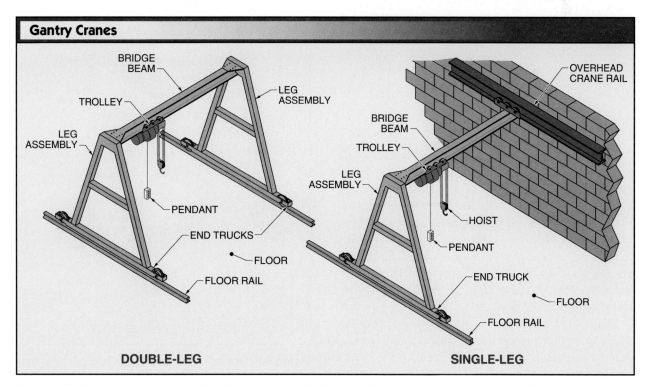

Figure 6-5. Gantry cranes consist of a hoist on a horizontal beam, which is supported by legs that roll along the floor.

Overhead Cranes

An *overhead crane* is an industrial crane that is composed of a bridge beam assembly that travels along a pair of overhead beams. An overhead crane is very similar in operation to a gantry crane. The primary difference between the two is the replacement of floor rails with overhead beams. An overhead crane's reach is anywhere within a rectangle defined by the horizontal lengths of travel.

The variations of overhead-crane designs have different arrangements for how the hoist travels on the bridge beam and how the bridge beam travels on the overhead beams. **See Figure 6-6.** A top-running hoist has a hoist that is installed in a trolley that travels along rails on top of a pair of bridge beams. In an underhung hoist, the hoist trolley travels on the upper surface of the lower flange of a single bridge girder.

The travel of the bridge-beam assembly along the overhead runways can also be either top-running or underhung. End trucks on top-running cranes travel on small-gauge railroad rails mounted on top of the overhead runways. A *runway* is a rail and beam combination. Top-running cranes with top-running hoists are the most common overhead crane configuration.

> ⚡ **Factoid**
>
> In 1888, Alton J. Shaw invented the first electric overhead traveling crane in Michigan. The third crane constructed by the Shaw Crane Company was purchased by the Union Pacific Railroad in 1888 and is still in use. Many of the improvements to crane operation are based on original innovations from the late 1800s and early 1900s.

Jib Cranes

A *jib crane* is an industrial crane that is composed of a cantilevered horizontal beam supported by a single structural leg. A *cantilever* is a projecting structure supported at only one end. The three basic types of jib-crane structures are wall-mounted, base-mounted, and mast. **See Figure 6-7.** Wall-mounted jib cranes are top-braced or cantilevered. Base-mounted jib cranes are freestanding cranes on a heavily anchored base mounting. Mast jib cranes have one structural leg (mast) mounted to both the floor and ceiling and a boom that is cantilevered, underbraced, or top-braced. A *boom* is a long beam that projects from the main part of a crane in order to extend the reach of the hoist.

The structure of a jib crane may be stationary or capable of rotation. Depending on the mount type, the rotation may be partial or a full 360°. The hoist trolley travels along the length of the boom. If the jib crane is stationary, the area of reach is limited to the linear boom footprint. If the jib crane is capable of rotation, the area of reach is an arc or full circle.

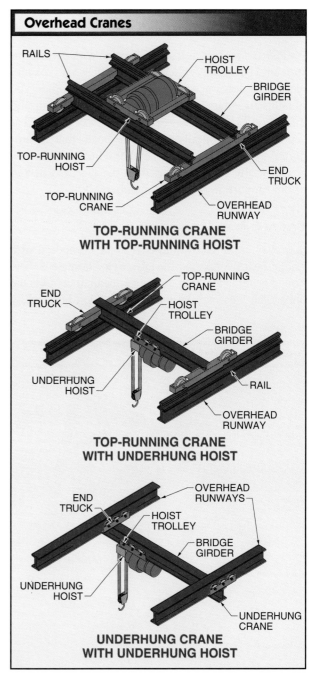

Figure 6-6. Overhead cranes are similar to gantry cranes except the hoist and bridge beam are supported by overhead beams.

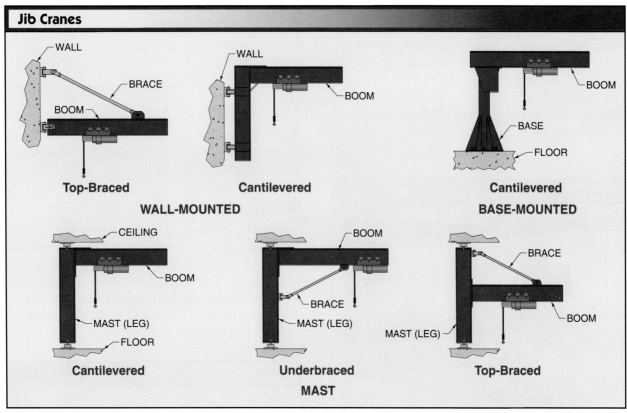

Figure 6-7. Jib-crane booms are supported at only one end but can be configured in several different designs.

Due to its cantilevered design, a jib crane is more vulnerable to overloading or damage. Slack should be taken up slowly before a lift to minimize shock to the crane boom. Rotating the boom on a jib crane should also be done slowly to prevent damage to the load, the surroundings, or individuals.

MOBILE CRANES

A *mobile crane* is a crane that can be moved between job sites. Mobile cranes are composed of crane assemblies and vehicle platforms. Many variations are available because the type of vehicle used is relatively independent of the crane. **See Figure 6-8.** The most common type of mobile crane is a motor truck, which has a platform similar to a typical flatbed truck. Motor trucks are often used on commercial or residential construction job sites that are accessible by roads. For off-road use, rough terrain or crawler vehicles allow the crane to operate in areas with soft or moderately uneven ground. Cranes are also available mounted on locomotive track vehicles.

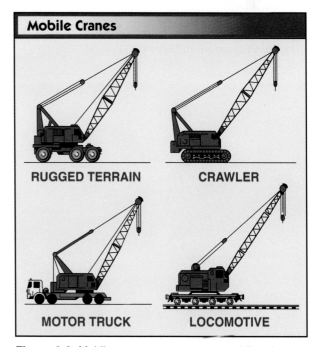

Figure 6-8. Mobile cranes are crane assemblies that are mounted on a mobile platform. The platform may use a variety of forms of mobility depending on the intended application.

Mobile cranes are designed to be small and light enough to be driven on typical roadways, but this limits their lifting capacity. A larger crane is able to lift heavier loads at a greater distance. Therefore, most mobile cranes use outriggers to increase their effective size. **See Figure 6-9.** An *outrigger* is an extendable support structure that increases a crane's footprint in order to improve stability.

Figure 6-9. An outrigger increases a mobile crane's footprint, which improves stability.

Lift-All Company, Inc.
The boom of a lattice-boom crane is assembled from lightweight structural members, but its grid-like construction provides significant strength.

Safety Tip

A mobile crane must be accurately leveled before making any lifts. This steadies the crane platform, improving lift safety. Leveling can be done by adjusting the heights of outriggers as needed.

The two most common types of cranes on mobile platforms are telescopic-boom cranes and lattice-boom cranes. Both of these crane types are available on a variety of vehicle platforms.

Telescopic-Boom Cranes

A *telescopic-boom crane* is a crane with an extendable boom composed of nested sections. The boom sections are extendable and retractable, allowing a wide range of boom lengths. **See Figure 6-10.** When fully retracted, the crane is easily transported on a street-legal vehicle. The boom movement and extension is typically powered by integrated hydraulic systems.

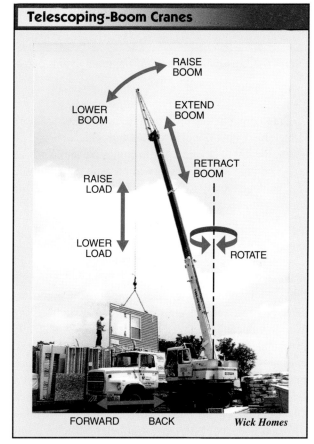

Figure 6-10. Telescoping-boom cranes have the ability to extend or retract the boom, providing significant versatility to its reach.

Lattice-Boom Cranes

A *lattice-boom crane* is a crane with a boom constructed from a gridwork of steel reinforcing members. The lattice structure provides a very strong boom that is light for its size. **See Figure 6-11.** The boom may be composed of one or multiple sections that must be assembled onto the crane body when on site. This makes a lattice-boom crane less transportable between sites, though its vehicle platform allows it to move around while on site. For this reason, lattice-boom cranes are often deployed for long-term use at large construction sites.

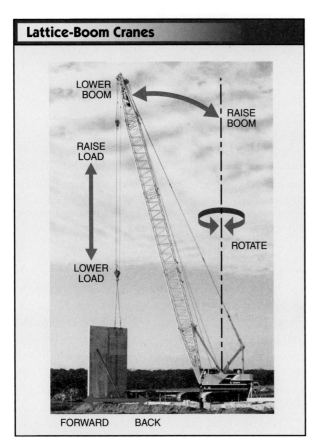

Figure 6-11. The boom of a lattice-boom crane is constructed of a lightweight, open structure that allows these cranes to have particularly long booms.

Crane Lift Capacities

A mobile crane may be specified by its maximum lift capacity, such as a "90-ton crane." However, because of the necessary horizontal reach for most lifts, the actual lifting capacity is likely much less. The capacity of a crane decreases the farther it must reach from its base because the moment (tipping) force increases.

See Figure 6-12. This distance is determined by the length and angle of the boom. The capacity at each point in the lift must be considered. For example, a certain load located 20′ from the crane must be moved to a new location 40′ away. Since the farther distance allows less lifting capacity, it determines the maximum allowable load weight for the entire lift.

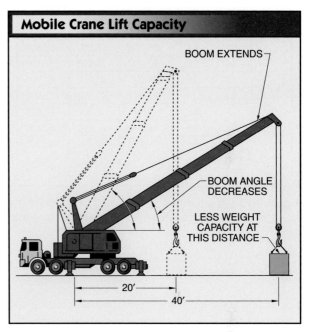

Figure 6-12. The lift capacity of a mobile crane is determined primarily by the horizontal distance of the load from the crane.

Other factors that affect the lift capacity are the amount of counterweight, the use of outriggers, and the direction of the boom in relation to the vehicle base (over the side or over the rear). Counterweights balance the moment (tipping) force caused by the load, so more counterweight increases the lifting capacity (to a point). Outriggers increase the effective footprint of the crane, improving stability. The direction of the boom also affects stability because cranes are typically not as wide as they are long. Tables of lift capacities that account for all of the applicable factors are available with the crane manufacturer's specifications and on cards located inside the operator's cab. **See Figure 6-13.**

Many cranes include an alarm that sounds if the attempted lift weight exceeds the lift capacity for the current boom length and orientation. This safety feature must never be ignored. Overloading a crane can damage the boom or cause the entire crane to tip over, which can result in injuries and property damage.

Lift Capacity Charts

Boom Length (ft)	Radius (ft)	Boom Angle (°)	Maximum Allowable Loads (lb)		
			With Outriggers	Without Outriggers	
				Over Side	Over Rear
40	12	73	220,000	100,400	139,700
	15	68	185,000	71,800	97,400
	20	60	149,000	48,100	54,600
	25	51	118,000	35,800	47,900
	30	41	86,000	28,300	37,800
	35	29	67,000	23,200	31,100
60	15	76	180,000	71,000	97,000
	20	71	147,000	47,300	63,900
	25	65	118,500	35,000	47,200
	30	60	86,200	27,500	37,100
	35	54	67,400	22,400	30,300
			54,700		25,500

Figure 6-13. Lift capacity tables are used to determine the maximum allowable load weight for a particular crane with certain lift distances.

CRANE INSPECTIONS

The inspection of a crane to ensure proper operation and safety falls roughly into three areas: the platform, the hoist positioning components, and the hoist. Each area can include complex machinery that requires many different types of inspection. The inspections required in each area may vary depending on the type of crane and its application.

On an industrial crane, the platform includes the structural support of the crane and any related floor or wall components. This structure should be inspected periodically for corrosion, distorted members, missing fasteners, or damaged welds. Rails along the floor or walls should be checked for clean, smooth surfaces and any damage from other equipment. On a mobile crane, the platform is the portion that provides mobility to the crane. Platforms are subject to any applicable vehicle maintenance and inspection activities, such as engine maintenance and tire inspection.

For industrial cranes, the positioning components are the hoist trolley and end trucks. The wheels should be checked for flat spots, cracks, and breaks. The wheel bearings should be checked for proper lubrication, intact seals, and physical damage. Periodic inspections should include checking the dimension between wheel flanges. **See Figure 6-14.** On most hoist trolleys, the dimension between

the flange landings of both wheels must be between ⅛″ and ¼″ greater than the beam flange width. The addition or removal of spacing washers may be necessary to obtain the proper dimension while keeping the hoist centered under the bridge beam. Some hoist trolleys are not adjustable.

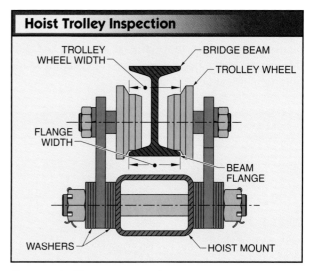

Hoist Trolley Inspection

TROLLEY WHEEL WIDTH — BRIDGE BEAM — TROLLEY WHEEL — FLANGE WIDTH — BEAM FLANGE — WASHERS — HOIST MOUNT

Figure 6-14. The inspection of a hoist trolley should include checking the spacing on trolley wheels. The wheels must be close enough to provide a secure attachment to the beam but not so close as to impede free travel.

Mobile cranes use booms to position the hoist directly over the load. As a structural component, booms should be inspected for physical damage such as bent members or corrosion. Boom systems also include complex actuation and control mechanisms, such as hydraulic cylinders. Frequent inspections should be made to check for low fluid levels, dirty filters, leaks, and stiff or unresponsive controls. More intensive periodic inspections may require the expertise of personnel that specialize in these power systems.

Though they are mounted in different ways, the basic components of a hoist are similar in all applications. Wire rope drums should be inspected for proper wrap, and hoist brakes should be tested for quick response. The manufacturer's literature should be checked for any cleaning or lubrication requirements. Any unusual noises, jerky operation, or unresponsive controls indicate problems with the hoist.

Crane operators, assistants, or other personnel involved in a lift should be alert for any problems with any of the equipment, both before and during a lift. If any problems are observed or suspected, the load and crane controls should be placed in safe positions and a supervisor should be immediately notified.

Appendix

KNOTS AND HITCHES

Fastening loads with a fiber rope normally requires some form of a knot or hitch. A *knot* is the interlacing of a part of a rope to itself, which is then drawn tight. Knots are designed to form a semipermanent connection that can be later untied. The sharp direction changes and pinching of the rope in a knot weakens the rope by as much as 55%. A *hitch* is the binding of rope to another object, usually temporarily. Hitches are designed for quick release.

Rope Terminology

Most rope terminology was derived from nautical (sailing) terms. **See Figure A-1.** A *bight* is a loose or slack part of a rope between two fixed ends. A *loop* is the folding or doubling of a line to create an opening through which another line may pass. A *nip* is a pressure point created when a rope crosses over itself after a turn around an object. A nip holds a knot together because its pressure, along with the friction of the rope material, keeps the rope from slipping through and loosening.

The portions of rope being worked are identified as working or standing. The *working part* is the portion of the rope involved in making the knot. The *working end* is the end of the working part. The working part of a rope is loose and the end can be passed through loops. The *standing part* is the portion of a rope that is unaltered or not involved in making a knot or hitch. The *standing end* is the end of the standing part. The standing end is often attached to some other item, making it taunt and unable to be worked.

Common Rigging Knots

Common rigging knots include the double hitch, half hitch, slip, bowline, and wagoner's hitch knots. A *double-hitch knot* is a knot composed of two half-hitch knots. **See Figure A-2.** A *half-hitch knot* is a knot where the working end is laid over the standing part and passed through the loop from the opposite side. Many knots use the basic half-hitch knot as one of the elements. The double turn of a double-hitch knot allows for two gripping nips. A half-hitch knot is formed by applying the following procedure:

1. Form a loop by crossing the working end over the standing part.
2. Tuck the working end under and through the loop.

A *slip knot* is a knot that can slip along the standing part of a rope to tighten a loop. **See Figure A-3.** When placed around an object, the loop of a slip knot is progressively tightened by strain on the standing part. A slip knot is formed by applying the following procedure:

1. Form a loop by placing the working end over the standing part.
2. Tuck the working end under and through loop.
3. Pass the standing part through loop.

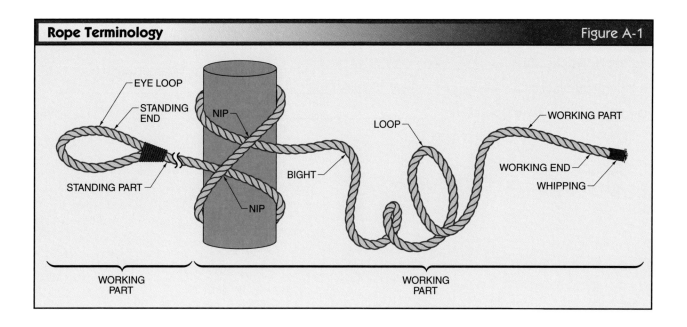

Rope Terminology   Figure A-1

EYE LOOP
STANDING END
NIP
LOOP
WORKING PART
STANDING PART
NIP
BIGHT
WORKING END
WHIPPING

WORKING PART   WORKING PART

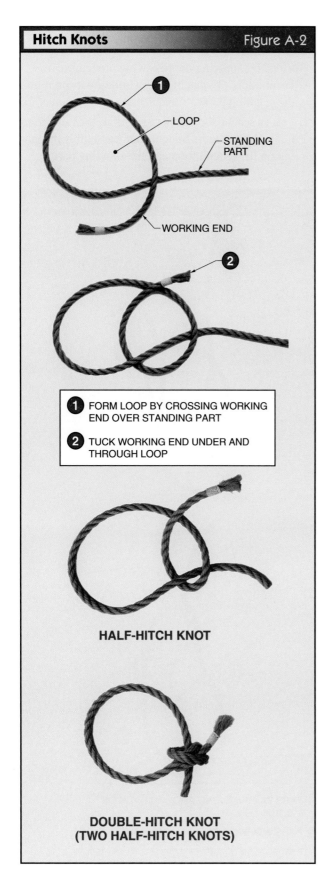

Hitch Knots — Figure A-2

1 LOOP
STANDING PART
WORKING END

2

1 FORM LOOP BY CROSSING WORKING END OVER STANDING PART

2 TUCK WORKING END UNDER AND THROUGH LOOP

HALF-HITCH KNOT

**DOUBLE-HITCH KNOT
(TWO HALF-HITCH KNOTS)**

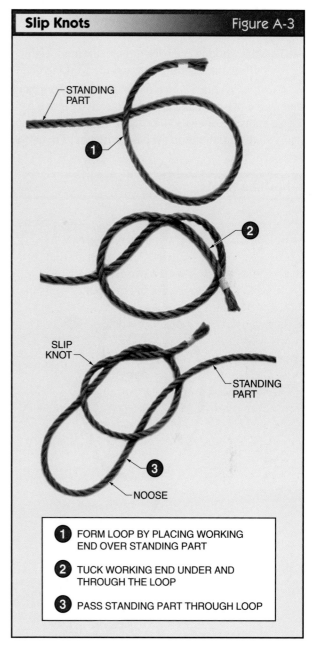

Slip Knots — Figure A-3

STANDING PART
1

2

SLIP KNOT
STANDING PART
3
NOOSE

1 FORM LOOP BY PLACING WORKING END OVER STANDING PART

2 TUCK WORKING END UNDER AND THROUGH THE LOOP

3 PASS STANDING PART THROUGH LOOP

A *bowline knot* is a knot that forms a loop that is fixed in size. **See Figure A-4.** As more strain is placed on the rope, the knot becomes stronger, but the loop does not tighten. When not under strain, the knot is easily released. A bowline knot is formed by applying the following procedure:

1. Loop the working part of rope over the standing part. Allow enough rope to form the size loop required.

2. Thread the working end beneath and through the loop.

3. Pass the working end around the back of the standing part.

4. Pass the working end back through the loop. Tighten by pulling the standing part and the working end.

A *wagoner's hitch knot* is a knot that provides a taunt line with a 3:1 mechanical advantage. **See Figure A-5.** These knots are often used for securing loads. There are many slight variations on the basic structure. Therefore,

there are also many names for similar knots, such as a trucker's hitch or power cinch. A wagoner's hitch knot is formed by applying the following procedure:

1. Form a loop by placing the working part on top of the standing part.

2. Form a second loop from the working part and insert it into the first loop. Snug the knot assembly by pulling on the second loop and the standing part.

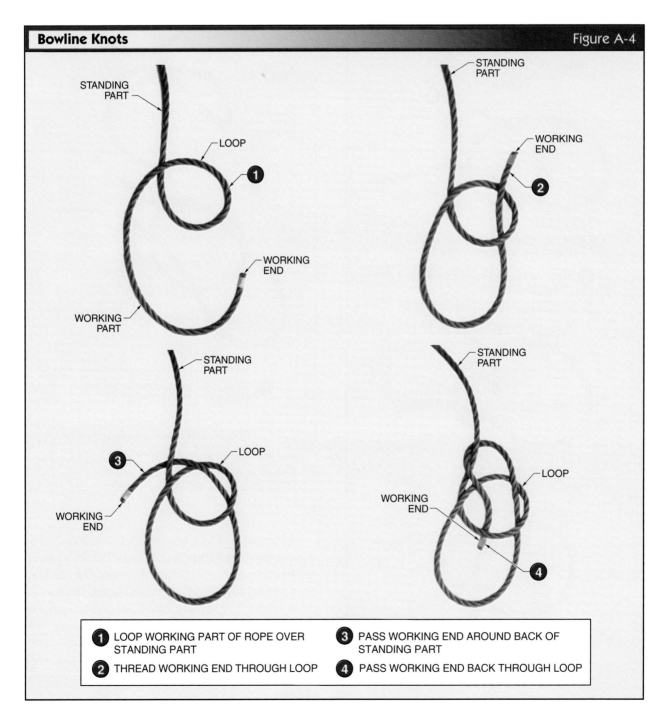

Bowline Knots　　　　　　　　　　　　　　Figure A-4

1. LOOP WORKING PART OF ROPE OVER STANDING PART
2. THREAD WORKING END THROUGH LOOP
3. PASS WORKING END AROUND BACK OF STANDING PART
4. PASS WORKING END BACK THROUGH LOOP

3. Bring the working end through the second loop, after passing through load-securing hooks or links.

4. Form the working end into a half knot and pull tight to secure the load.

Common rigging hitches include the timber hitch, clove hitch, cow hitch, cat's-paw hitch, scaffold hitch, and blackwall hitch. These hitches allow a rigger to form a tight bind that is easily released after the lift.

A *timber hitch* is a hitch used to wrap and drag lengthy material. **See Figure A-6.** This hitch can loosen when lifting, but may be used to pull long material such as logs, pipes, or beams, horizontally. A timber hitch gets its gripping power from the many nips against the material. A timber hitch is formed by applying the following procedure:

1. Loop the working end around the standing part.

2. Twist the working end around its side of the loop three to five times.

3. Pull the working end tight.

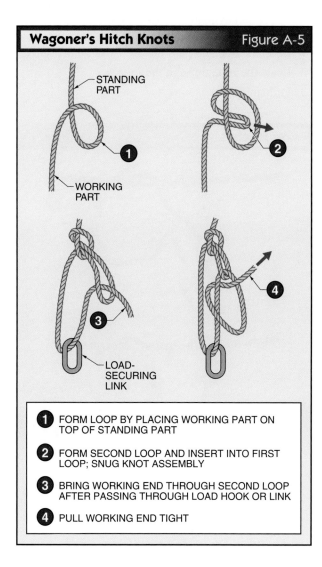

Wagoner's Hitch Knots — Figure A-5

STANDING PART

WORKING PART

LOAD-SECURING LINK

1. FORM LOOP BY PLACING WORKING PART ON TOP OF STANDING PART

2. FORM SECOND LOOP AND INSERT INTO FIRST LOOP; SNUG KNOT ASSEMBLY

3. BRING WORKING END THROUGH SECOND LOOP AFTER PASSING THROUGH LOAD HOOK OR LINK

4. PULL WORKING END TIGHT

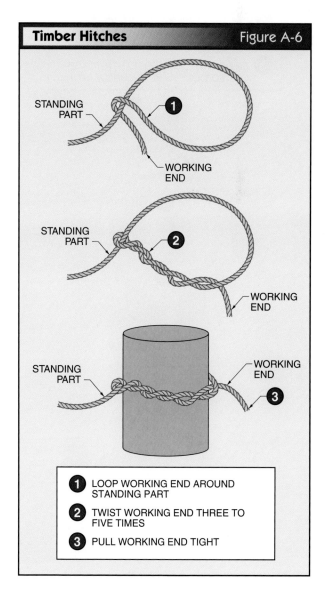

Timber Hitches — Figure A-6

STANDING PART

WORKING END

STANDING PART

WORKING END

STANDING PART

WORKING END

1. LOOP WORKING END AROUND STANDING PART

2. TWIST WORKING END THREE TO FIVE TIMES

3. PULL WORKING END TIGHT

Common Rigging Hitches

Hitches work by the pressure of rope being pressed together. The standing part of the rope is nipped (jammed) over the working part. The friction of the nip causes the working part to be bound as the standing part is pulled, which prevents the working part from slipping through. Due to the reliance on friction, hitches should never be formed with slippery rope, including some synthetic ropes.

A *clove hitch* is a hitch used to secure a rope temporarily to an object. **See Figure A-7.** A clove hitch is useful because it is attached quickly, holds firmly, and has a rapid release. Clove hitches can be formed at the working end, or in the middle of a rope, if the loops can be slipped over one end of the object. A clove hitch is formed by applying the following procedure:

1. Cross one hand over the other and grasp the rope with both hands.

2. Uncross the hands to form two loops.

3. Bring the loops together. Place over the object to be secured.

A *cow hitch* is a hitch composed of a pair of half hitches formed in opposing directions. **See Figure A-8.** A cow hitch is often made to quickly attach a tag line to a load. A *tag line* is a rope, handled by an individual, to control rotational movement of a load during lifting. A cow hitch is made and released easily but is firm enough to steady loads. A cow hitch is formed by applying the following procedure:

1. Loop the line and pass the loop around the object.

2. Draw the rope through the loop.

3. Pull snug.

Clove Hitches   Figure A-7

1. CROSS HANDS AND GRASP ROPE
2. UNCROSS HANDS TO FORM TWO LOOPS
3. BRING THE LOOPS TOGETHER; PLACE OVER OBJECT TO BE SECURED

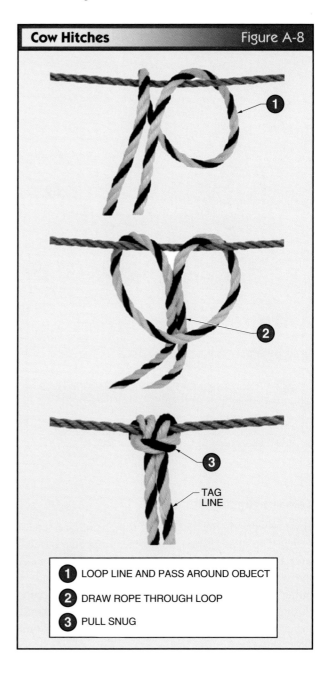

Cow Hitches   Figure A-8

TAG LINE

1. LOOP LINE AND PASS AROUND OBJECT
2. DRAW ROPE THROUGH LOOP
3. PULL SNUG

A *cat's-paw hitch* is a hitch used as a quickly formed, light-duty eye. **See Figure A-9.** It is similar to a cow hitch, but the additional twists on each side add stability. A cat's-paw hitch is formed by applying the following procedure:

1. Grasp the rope with both hands. Leave plenty of bight.

2. Rotate hands in opposite directions and continue to rotate the two loops for two complete turns.

3. Place the eye over the end of a hook.

A *scaffold hitch* is a hitch used to hang or support planks or beams. **See Figure A-10.** A scaffold hitch is made from a combination of a clove hitch and a bowline knot. A scaffold hitch is formed by applying the following procedure:

1. Attach a clove hitch to the object.

2. Tie the working end to the standing part using a bowline knot.

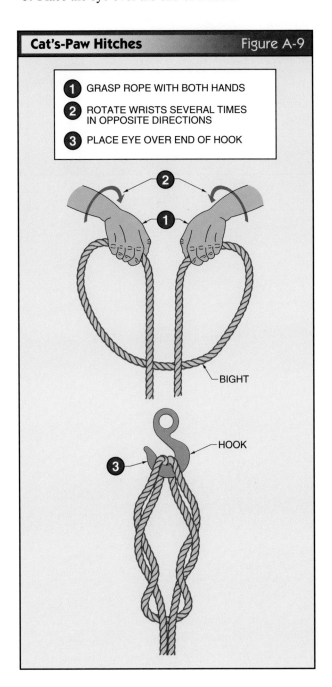

Cat's-Paw Hitches Figure A-9

1. GRASP ROPE WITH BOTH HANDS
2. ROTATE WRISTS SEVERAL TIMES IN OPPOSITE DIRECTIONS
3. PLACE EYE OVER END OF HOOK

BIGHT

HOOK

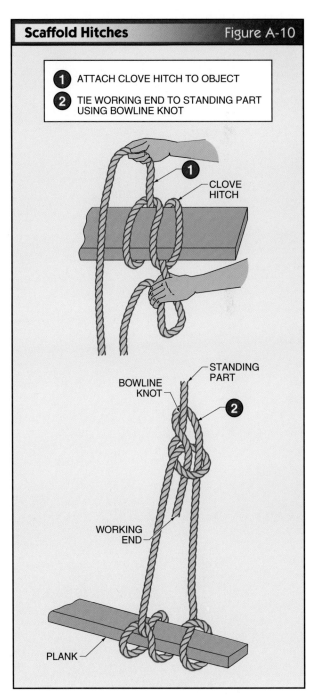

Scaffold Hitches Figure A-10

1. ATTACH CLOVE HITCH TO OBJECT
2. TIE WORKING END TO STANDING PART USING BOWLINE KNOT

CLOVE HITCH

STANDING PART

BOWLINE KNOT

WORKING END

PLANK

A *blackwall hitch* is a hitch that secures a rope to a hoisting hook. **See Figure A-11.** This hitch is made from a simple half hitch over a hook, which holds only when under tension. A blackwall hitch should only be made from a natural fiber rope because synthetic ropes may slip. A blackwall hitch is formed by applying the following procedure:

1. Pass the working end twice around the shank of a hook.

2. Cross it under the standing part in the mouth of the hook.

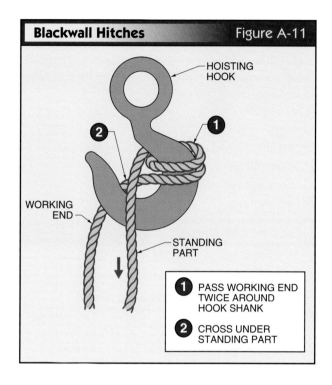

Blackwall Hitches   Figure A-11

HOISTING HOOK

WORKING END

STANDING PART

1 PASS WORKING END TWICE AROUND HOOK SHANK

2 CROSS UNDER STANDING PART

Common U.S. Customary Units

	Unit	Abbreviation	Equivalents
Length	inch	in. *or* "	0.083 ft *or* 0.028 yd
	foot	ft *or* '	12 in. *or* 0.33 yd
	yard	yd	36 in. *or* 3 ft
Area	square inch	sq in. *or* in^2	0.0069 sq ft *or* 0.00077 sq yd
	square foot	sq ft *or* ft^2	144 sq in. *or* 0.11 sq yd
	square yard	sq yd *or* yd^2	1296 sq in. *or* 9 sq ft
Volume	cubic inch	cu in. *or* in^3	0.00058 cu ft *or* 0.000021 cu yd
	cubic foot	cu ft *or* ft^3	1728 cu in. *or* 0.037 cu yd
	cubic yard	cu yd *or* yd^3	46,659 cu in. *or* 27 cu ft
Weight	pound	lb *or* #	0.0005 t
	ton*	t	2000 lb

* known as a short ton outside of U.S.

Common Metric Units

	Unit	Abbreviation	Equivalents
Length	centimeter	cm	0.01 m *or* 0.00001 km
	meter	m	100 cm *or* 0.001 km
	kilometer	km	100,000 cm *or* 1000 m
Area	square centimeter	cm^2	0.0001 m^2
	square meter	m^2	10,000 cm^2
Volume	cubic centimeter	cm^3	0.000001 m^3 *or* 0.001 l
	cubic meter	m^3	1,000,000 cm^3 *or* 1000 l
	liter	l	1000 cm^3 *or* 0.001 m^3
Mass	kilogram	kg	0.001 t
	metric ton	t	1000 kg

Unit Conversions

	U.S. Customary to Metric	Metric to U.S. Customary
Length	1 ft = 0.305 m	1 m = 3.28 ft
Area	1 ft^2 = 0.0929 m^2	1 m^2 = 10.8 ft^2
Volume	1 ft^3 = 0.0283 m^3	1 m^3 = 35.3 ft^3
Weight and Mass	1 lb = 0.454 kg	1 kg = 2.20 lb

Metric Prefixes

Multiples and Submultiples	Prefixes	Symbols	Meaning
$1{,}000{,}000{,}000{,}000 = 10^{12}$	tera	T	trillion
$1{,}000{,}000{,}000 = 10^{9}$	giga	G	billion
$1{,}000{,}000 = 10^{6}$	mega	M	million
$1{,}000 = 10^{3}$	kilo	k	thousand
$100 = 10^{2}$	hecto	h	hundred
$10 = 10^{1}$	deka	da	ten
$1 = 10^{0}$			
$0.1 = 10^{-1}$	deci	d	tenth
$0.01 = 10^{-2}$	centi	c	hundredth
$0.001 = 10^{-3}$	milli	m	thousandth
$0.000001 = 10^{-6}$	micro	μ	millionth
$0.000000001 = 10^{-9}$	nano	n	billionth
$0.000000000001 = 10^{-12}$	pico	p	trillionth

Electrical Conduit Weights*

Trade Size	Steel EMT	Steel IMC	Steel Rigid	Aluminum Rigid	PVC Rigid
½	0.300	0.620	0.820	0.281	0.164
¾	0.460	0.840	1.090	0.374	0.218
1	0.670	1.19	1.610	0.545	0.321
1¼	1.01	1.58	2.18	0.716	0.434
1½	1.16	1.94	2.63	0.887	0.518
2	1.48	2.56	3.50	1.19	0.695
2½	2.16	4.41	5.59	1.88	1.10
3	2.63	5.43	7.27	2.46	1.44
3½	3.49	6.29	8.80	2.96	1.73
4	3.93	7.00	10.3	3.50	2.04
5	—	—	14.0	4.79	2.78
6	—	—	18.4	6.30	3.60

* in lb/ft

Stock Material Weights*

Material	Weight	Material	Weight	Material	Weight
METALS		Chestnut	30	Granite	172
Aluminum, cast hammered	165	Cypress, southern	32	Greenstone, trap	187
Aluminum, bronze	481	Douglas fir	34	Gypsum, alabaster	159
Antimony	416	Elm, American	35	Limestone	160
Arsenic	358	Hemlock, eastern or western	28	Magnesite	187
Bismuth	608	Hickory	53	Marble	168
Brass, cast-rolled	534	Larch, western	36	Phosphate rock, apatite	200
Chromium	428	Maple, red or black	38 – 40	Pumice, natural	40
Cobalt	552	Oak	51	Quartz, flint	165
Copper, cast-rolled	556	Pine	27 – 28	Sandstone, bluestone	147
Gold, cast-hammered	1205	Poplar, yellow	28	Slate, shale	172
Iron, cast pig	450	Redwood	30	Soapstone, talc	169
Iron, wrought	485	Spruce	28	**BITUMINOUS SUBSTANCES**	
Iron, slag	172	Tamarack	37	Asphaltum	81
Lead	706	Walnut	39 – 40	Coal, anthracite	97
Magnesium	109	**LIQUIDS**		Coal, bituminous	84
Manganese	456	Alcohol, 100%	49	Coal, lignite	78
Mercury	848	Acid, muriatic (40%)	75	Coal, coke	75
Molybdenum	562	Acid, nitric (91%)	94	Graphite	131
Nickel	545	Acid, sulphuric (87%)	112	Paraffin	56
Platinum, cast-hammered	1330	Lye, soda (66%)	106	Petroleum, crude	55
Silver, cast-hammered	656	Oils	58	Petroleum, refined	50
Steel	490	Petroleum	55	Pitch	69
Tin, cast-hammered	459	Gasoline	42	Tar, bituminous	75
Tungsten	1180	Water, at 4°C	62	**BRICK MASONRY**	
Vanadium	350	Water, ice	56	Pressed brick	140
Zinc, cast-rolled	440	Water, fresh snow	8	Common brick	120
OTHER SOLIDS		Water, sea water	64	Soft brick	100
Carbon, amorphous	129	**GASES**		**CONCRETE**	
Cork	15	Air, at 0°C	0.08071	Cement, stone, sand	144
Ebony	76	Ammonia	0.0478	Cement, slag, etc.	130
Fats	58	Carbon dioxide	0.1234	Cement, cinder, etc.	100
Glass, common plate	160	Carbon monoxide	0.0781	**BUILDING MATERIAL**	
Glass, crystal	184	Gas, natural	0.038 – 0.039	Ashes, cinders	40 – 45
Phosphorous, white	114	Hydrogen	0.00559	Cement, Portland (loose)	90
Resins, rosin or amber	67	Nitrogen	0.0784	Cement, Portland (set)	183
Rubber	58	Oxygen	0.0892	Lime, gypsum (loose)	65 – 75
Silicon	155	**MINERALS**		Mortar, set	103
Sulphur, amorphous	128	Asbestos	153	Slags, bank slag	67 – 72
Wax	60	Basalt	184	Slags, screenings	98 – 117
TIMBER, U.S. SEASONED		Bauxite	159	Slags, machine slag	96
Ash, white	41	Borax	109	**EARTH**	
Beech	44	Chalk	137	Clay, damp	110
Birch, yellow	43	Clay	137	Dry, packed	95
Cedar, white or red	22 – 23	Dolomite	181	Mud, packed	115

* in lb/cu ft

Regular-Nut Eyebolts

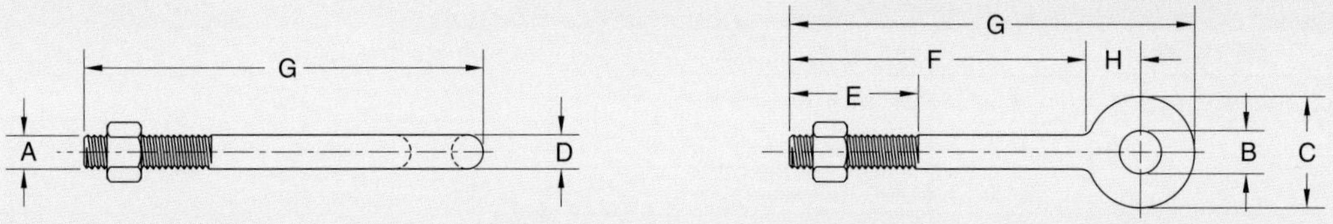

Shank Diameter and Length*	G-291 Stock No. Galv	Working Load Limit†	Weight per 100†	Dimensions*							
				A	B	C	D	E	F	G	H
¼ × 2	1043230	650	6.00	0.25	0.50	1.00	0.25	1.50	2.00	3.06	0.56
¼ × 4	1043258	650	13.50	0.25	0.50	1.00	0.25	2.50	4.00	5.06	0.56
5⁄16 × 2¼	1043276	1200	18.75	0.31	0.62	1.25	0.31	1.50	2.25	3.56	0.69
5⁄16 × 4¼	1043294	1200	25.00	0.31	0.62	1.25	0.31	2.50	4.25	5.56	0.69
⅜ × 2½	1043310	1550	24.33	0.38	0.75	1.50	0.38	1.50	2.50	4.12	0.88
⅜ × 4½	1043338	1550	37.50	0.38	0.75	1.50	0.38	2.50	4.50	6.12	0.88
⅜ × 6	1043356	1550	43.75	0.38	0.75	1.50	0.38	2.50	6.00	7.62	0.88
½ × 3¼	1043374	2600	50.00	0.50	1.00	2.00	0.50	1.50	3.25	5.38	1.12
½ × 6	1043392	2600	62.50	0.50	1.00	2.00	0.50	3.00	6.00	8.12	1.12
½ × 8	1043418	2600	75.00	0.50	1.00	2.00	0.50	3.00	8.00	10.12	1.12
½ × 10	1043436	2600	88.00	0.50	1.00	2.00	0.50	3.00	10.00	12.12	1.12
½ × 12	1043454	2600	100.00	0.50	1.00	2.00	0.50	3.00	12.00	14.12	1.12
⅝ × 4	1043472	5200	101.25	0.62	1.25	2.50	0.62	2.00	4.00	6.69	1.44
⅝ × 6	1043490	5200	120.00	0.62	1.25	2.50	0.62	3.00	6.00	8.69	1.44
⅝ × 8	1043515	5200	131.00	0.62	1.25	2.50	0.62	3.00	8.00	10.69	1.44
⅝ × 10	1043533	5200	162.50	0.62	1.25	2.50	0.62	3.00	10.00	12.69	1.44
⅝ × 12	1043551	5200	175.00	0.62	1.25	2.50	0.62	4.00	12.00	14.69	1.44
¾ × 4½	1043579	7200	185.90	0.75	1.50	3.00	0.75	2.00	4.50	7.69	1.69
¾ × 6	1043597	7200	180.00	0.75	1.50	3.00	0.75	3.00	6.00	9.19	1.69
¾ × 8	1043613	7200	200.00	0.75	1.50	3.00	0.75	3.00	8.00	11.19	1.69
¾ × 10	1043631	7200	237.50	0.75	1.50	3.00	0.75	3.00	10.00	13.19	1.69
¾ × 12	1043659	7200	251.94	0.75	1.50	3.00	0.75	4.00	12.00	15.19	1.69
¾ × 15	1043677	7200	300.00	0.75	1.50	3.00	0.75	5.00	15.00	18.19	1.69
⅞ × 5	1043695	10,600	275.00	0.88	1.75	3.50	0.88	2.50	5.00	8.75	2.00
⅞ × 8	1043711	10,600	325.00	0.88	1.75	3.50	0.88	4.00	8.00	11.75	2.00
⅞ × 12	1043739	10,600	400.00	0.88	1.75	3.50	0.88	4.00	12.00	15.75	2.00
1 × 6	1043757	13,300	425.00	1.00	2.00	4.00	1.00	3.00	6.00	10.31	2.31
1 × 9	1043775	13,300	452.00	1.00	2.00	4.00	1.00	4.00	9.00	13.31	2.31
1 × 12	1043793	13,300	550.00	1.00	2.00	4.00	1.00	4.00	12.00	16.31	2.31
1 × 18	1043819	13,300	650.00	1.00	2.00	4.00	1.00	7.00	18.00	22.31	2.31
1¼ × 8	1043837	21,000	750.00	1.25	2.50	5.00	1.25	4.00	8.00	13.38	2.88
1¼ × 12	1043855	21,000	900.00	1.25	2.50	5.00	1.25	4.00	12.00	17.38	2.88
1¼ × 20	1043873	21,000	1150.00	1.25	2.50	5.00	1.25	6.00	20.00	25.38	2.88

* in in.
† in lb

Shoulder-Nut Eyebolts

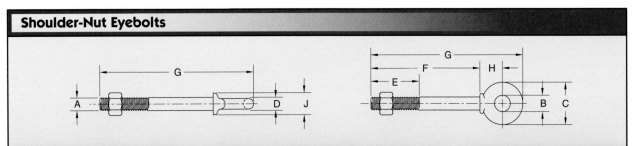

Shank Diameter and Length*	G-277 Stock No. Galv	Working Load Limit†	Weight per 100†	Dimensions*								
				A	B	C	D	E	F	G	H	J
¼ × 2	1045014	650	6.61	0.25	0.50	0.88	0.19	1.50	2.00	2.94	0.50	0.47
¼ × 4	1045032	650	8.61	0.25	0.50	0.88	0.19	2.50	4.00	4.94	0.50	0.47
⁵⁄₁₆ × 2¼	1045050	1200	12.50	0.31	0.62	1.12	0.25	1.50	2.25	3.50	0.69	0.56
⁵⁄₁₆ × 4¼	1045078	1200	18.75	0.31	0.62	1.12	0.25	2.50	4.25	5.50	0.69	0.56
⅜ × 2½	1045096	1550	19.00	0.38	0.75	1.38	0.31	1.50	2.50	3.97	0.78	0.66
⅜ × 4½	1045112	1550	31.58	0.38	0.75	1.38	0.31	2.50	4.50	5.97	0.78	0.66
½ × 3¼	1045130	2600	37.50	0.50	1.00	1.75	0.38	1.50	3.25	5.12	1.00	0.91
½ × 6	1045158	2600	56.25	0.50	1.00	1.75	0.38	3.00	6.00	7.88	1.00	0.91
⅝ × 4	1045176	5200	75.00	0.62	1.25	2.25	0.50	2.00	4.00	6.44	1.31	1.12
⅝ × 6	1045194	5200	100.25	0.62	1.25	2.25	0.50	3.00	6.00	8.44	1.31	1.12
¾ × 4½	1045210	7200	125.00	0.75	1.50	2.75	0.62	2.00	4.50	7.44	1.56	1.38
¾ × 6	1045238	7200	150.00	0.75	1.50	2.75	0.62	3.00	6.00	8.94	1.56	1.38
⅞ × 5	1045256	10,650	225.00	0.88	1.75	3.25	0.75	2.50	5.00	8.46	1.84	1.56
1 × 6	1045292	10,650	375.00	1.00	2.00	3.75	0.88	3.00	6.00	9.97	2.09	1.81
1 × 9	1045318	13,300	429.00	1.00	2.00	3.75	0.88	4.00	9.00	12.97	2.09	1.81
1¼ × 8	1045336	13,300	650.00	1.25	2.50	4.50	1.00	4.00	8.00	12.72	2.47	2.28
1¼ × 12	1045354	21,000	775.00	1.25	2.50	4.50	1.00	4.00	12.00	16.72	2.47	2.28
1½ × 15	1045372	24,000	1425.00	1.50	3.00	5.50	1.25	6.00	15.00	20.75	3.00	2.75

* in in.
† in lb

Machinery Eyebolts

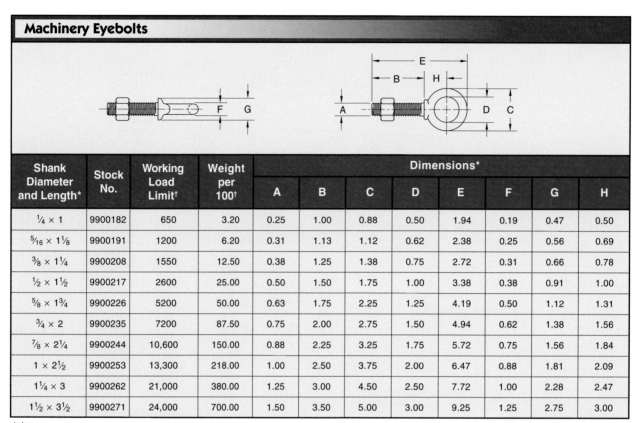

Shank Diameter and Length*	Stock No.	Working Load Limit†	Weight per 100†	Dimensions*							
				A	B	C	D	E	F	G	H
¼ × 1	9900182	650	3.20	0.25	1.00	0.88	0.50	1.94	0.19	0.47	0.50
⁵⁄₁₆ × 1⅛	9900191	1200	6.20	0.31	1.13	1.12	0.62	2.38	0.25	0.56	0.69
⅜ × 1¼	9900208	1550	12.50	0.38	1.25	1.38	0.75	2.72	0.31	0.66	0.78
½ × 1½	9900217	2600	25.00	0.50	1.50	1.75	1.00	3.38	0.38	0.91	1.00
⅝ × 1¾	9900226	5200	50.00	0.63	1.75	2.25	1.25	4.19	0.50	1.12	1.31
¾ × 2	9900235	7200	87.50	0.75	2.00	2.75	1.50	4.94	0.62	1.38	1.56
⅞ × 2¼	9900244	10,600	150.00	0.88	2.25	3.25	1.75	5.72	0.75	1.56	1.84
1 × 2½	9900253	13,300	218.00	1.00	2.50	3.75	2.00	6.47	0.88	1.81	2.09
1¼ × 3	9900262	21,000	380.00	1.25	3.00	4.50	2.50	7.72	1.00	2.28	2.47
1½ × 3½	9900271	24,000	700.00	1.50	3.50	5.00	3.00	9.25	1.25	2.75	3.00

* in in.
† in lb

Rated Capacities of Web Slings in Vertical Hitches*

Plies	Width†	Class 5 Webbing		Class 7 Webbing	
		Types 1, 2, 3, and 4	Type 5	Types 1, 2, 3, and 4	Type 5
1 Ply	1	1100	2200	1600	3200
	2	2200	4400	3100	6200
	3	3300	6600	4700	9400
	4	4400	8800	6200	12,400
	6	6600	13,200	9300	18,600
	8	—	—	11,800	21,200
	10	—	—	14,700	26,500
	12	—	—	17,600	31,800
2 Ply	1	2200	4400	3100	6200
	2	4400	8800	6200	12,400
	3	6600	13,200	8800	17,600
	4	8200	16,400	11,000	22,000
	6	12,300	24,600	16,500	33,000
	8	—	—	22,700	42,300
	10	—	—	28,400	52,900
	12	—	—	34,100	63,500
4 Ply	1	Not Typically Available	Not Typically Available	5500	11,000
	2			11,000	22,000
	3			16,400	32,900
	4			20,400	40,800
	6			30,600	61,200

* in lb, with a safety factor of 5. Type 6 rated capacities vary by manufacturer.
† in in.

Rated Capacities of Round Slings*

Round Sling Size	Color Code	Sling Hitch			
		Vertical	Choker	Vertical Basket	45° Basket
1	Purple	2600	2100	5200	3700
2	Green	5300	4200	10,600	7500
3	Yellow	8400	6700	16,800	11,900
4	Tan	10,600	8500	21,200	15,000
5	Red	13,200	10,600	26,400	18,700
6	White	16,800	13,400	33,600	23,800
7	Blue	21,200	17,000	42,400	30,000
8	Orange	25,000	20,000	50,000	35,400
9	Orange	31,000	24,800	62,000	43,800
10	Orange	40,000	32,000	80,000	56,600
11	Orange	53,000	42,400	106,000	74,900
12	Orange	66,000	52,800	132,000	93,000

* in lb

Rated Capacities of Chain*

Grade	Chain Size†	90° Vertical Load	60° Vertical Load	45° Vertical Load	30° Vertical Load	60° Quad Leg Load	45° Quad Leg Load	30° Quad Leg Load
80	7/32	2100	3600	3000	2100	5450	4450	3150
	9/32	3500	6100	4900	3500	9100	7400	5200
	3/8	7100	12,300	10,000	7100	18,400	15,100	10,600
	1/2	12,000	20,800	17,000	12,000	31,200	25,500	18,000
	5/8	18,100	31,300	25,600	18,100	47,000	38,400	27,100
	3/4	28,300	49,000	40,000	28,300	73,500	60,000	42,400
	7/8	34,200	59,200	48,400	34,200	88,900	72,500	51,300
	1	47,700	82,600	67,400	47,700	123,900	101,200	71,500
	1 1/4	72,300	125,200	102,200	72,300	187,800	153,400	108,400
100	7/32	2700	4700	3800	2700	7000	5700	4000
	9/32	4300	7400	6100	4300	11,200	9100	6400
	3/8	8800	15,200	12,400	8800	22,900	18,700	13,200
	1/2	15,000	26,000	21,200	15,000	39,000	31,800	22,500
	5/8	22,600	39,100	32,000	22,600	58,700	47,900	33,900
	3/4	35,300	61,100	49,900	35,300	91,700	74,900	53,000

* in lb
† in in.

Electric Hoist Checklist

Item	Daily	Monthly	Semi-annually	Deficiencies
All functional operating mechanisms	✓	✓	✓	Maladjustment interfering with proper operation, excessive component wear
Controls	✓		✓	Improper operation
Safety Devices	✓		✓	Malfunction
Hooks	✓	✓	✓	Deformation, chemical damage, 15% in excess of normal throat opening, 10% twist from plane of unbent hook, cracks
Load-bearing components (except rope or chain)	✓	✓	✓	Damage (especially if hook is twisted or pulling open)
Load-bearing rope	✓	✓	✓	Wear, twist, distortion, improper dead-ending, deposits of foreign material
Load-bearing chain	✓	✓	✓	Wear, twist, distortion, improper dead-ending, deposits of foreign material
Fasteners	✓	✓	✓	Not tight
Drums, pulleys, sprockets			✓	Cracks, excessive wear
Pins, bearings, shafts, gears, rollers, locking and clamping devices			✓	Cracks, excessive wear, distortion, corrosion
Brakes	✓		✓	Excessive wear, drift
Electrical			✓	Pitting, loose wires
Contactors, limit switches, pushbutton stations			✓	Deterioration, contact wear, loose wires
Hook retaining members (collars, nuts) and pins, welds, or rivets securing them			✓	Not tight or secure
Supporting structure or trolley			✓	Continued ability to support imposed loads
Warning label	✓		✓	Removed or illegible
Pushbutton markings	✓		✓	Removed or illegible
Capacity marking	✓		✓	Removed or illegible

Hoisting Equipment Checklist

1. Prior to Installation:

❑ Check for any possible damage during shipment. Do not install a damaged hoist.

❑ Check all lubricant levels.

❑ Check wire rope for damage if hoist wire-rope type. Be sure wire rope is properly seated in drum grooves and sheaves.

❑ Check chain for damage if hoist is chain type. Be sure chain properly enters sprockets and chain guiding points.

❑ Check to be sure that power supply shown on serial plate of hoist is the same as the power supply planned for connection to the hoist.

2. Installation:

❑ Install stationary mounting or trolley mounting to monorail beam exactly as instructed by the manufacturer's instructions.

❑ Check supporting structure, including monorail, to make sure it has a load rating equal to that of the hoist installed.

3. Power Supply:

❑ Make sure all electrical connections are made in accordance with manufacturer's wiring diagram, which is usually found inside the cover of the control enclosure.

❑ Make sure electrical supply system is in compliance with the National Electrical Code®.

4. Phase Connections:

❑ Depress the UP button on the pendant control to determine the direction of hook travel. If hook travel is upward, the hoist is properly phased. If it is downward, discontinue operation until phasing is corrected.

❑ Correct power connections if hoist is improperly phased by changing any two power line leads to the hoist. Never change internal wiring connections in the hoist or pendant control.

❑ Recheck operation of hoist after interchanging power line leads to confirm proper direction of motion.

5. Upper Limit Switch:

❑ Raise unloaded hook until it is approximately 1' below the upper limit switch trip point. Slowly jog hook upward until hook can be raised no further. Lower block about 2' and raise without jogging until limit switch trips and hook can be raised no further.

❑ Disconnect power supply and check all electrical connections if upper limit switch does not operate, or trip point is too close to hoist.

❑ Make any necessary adjustments.

❑ Reconnect power supply and recheck hoist operation after checking connections or making adjustments.

6. Lower Limit Switch:

❑ Check operation of hoist having a lower limit switch in same manner as for one with an upper limit switch. Never adjust lower limit switch to a point where less than one wrap of wire rope remains on the drum.

7. Lower Hook Travel (when hoist does not have lower limit switch):

❑ Lower the unloaded hook to its lowest possible operating point, or, for wire rope hoists, until two full wraps of wire remain on the drum.

❑ If it appears that less than two wraps of wire rope will be on the drum at the lowest possible operating point, the hoist cannot be installed or used unless it is equipped with a lower limit device.

8. Trolley Operation:

❑ Operate a trolley-mounted hoist over its entire travel distance on a monorail beam while the hoist is unloaded to check all clearances and verify that no interference occurs.

9. Braking System:

❑ Raise and lower hook, without load, stopping the motion at several points to test the operation of the brakes.

❑ Raise hook with capacity load several inches and stop to check that brake holds the load and that the load does not drift downward. If drift does not occur, raise and lower hook with capacity load, stopping the motion at several points to test the operation of the brakes.

10. Load Test:

❑ Load test the hoist with a load equal to 125% of the rated capacity load. If the hoist is equipped with a load limiting device that prevents the lifting of 125% of the rated load, testing should be accomplished with a load equal to 100% of the rated capacity load, followed by a test to check the function of the load limiting device.

11. Filing the Report:

❑ Prepare written report outlining installation procedures, problems encountered, and results of all checks and tests conducted. This report should indicate the approval or certification of the equipment for plant use, and should be signed by the responsible individual and filed in the equipment folder.

12. Operating Instructions:

❑ Issue instructions for hoist operators based on instructions and warning in hoist manufacturer's manual.

❑ Check warning tag or label on the hoist and make sure it stays there. Warning tag is a recent code requirement for new equipment. It is highly recommended for existing equipment. The warning tag should contain the following message:

WARNING:

To avoid injury, do not:

- lift more than rated load
- lift people or load over people
- operate with twisted, kinked, or damaged rope or chain
- operate damaged or malfunctioning hoist
- make side pulls that misalign rope or chain with hoist
- operate if rope is not seated in groove or chain in pockets
- operate unless travel devices limit function; test each shift
- operate hand-powered hoist except with hand power

Hand Signals for Crane Operators

HOIST. WITH FOREARM VERTICAL, FOREFINGER POINTING UP, MOVE HAND IN SMALL HORIZONTAL CIRCLES.

LOWER. WITH ARM EXTENDED DOWNWARD, FOREFINGER POINTING DOWN, MOVE HAND IN SMALL HORIZONTAL CIRCLES.

RAISE BOOM. ARM EXTENDED, FINGERS CLOSED, THUMB POINTING UPWARD.

LOWER BOOM. ARM EXTENDED, FINGERS CLOSED, THUMB POINTING DOWN.

EXTEND BOOM. BOTH FISTS IN FRONT OF BODY WITH THUMBS POINTING OUTWARD. (TELESCOPIC BOOMS ONLY.)

RETRACT BOOM. BOTH FISTS IN FRONT OF BODY WITH THUMBS POINTING TOWARD EACH OTHER. (TELESCOPIC BOOM ONLY.)

RAISE BOOM AND LOWER LOAD. WITH ARM EXTENDED, THUMB POINTING UP, FLEX FINGERS IN AND OUT AS LONG AS THE LOAD MOVEMENT IS DESIRED.

LOWER BOOM AND RAISE LOAD. WITH ARM EXTENDED, THUMB POINTING DOWN, FLEX FINGERS IN AND OUT AS LONG AS LOAD MOVEMENT IS DESIRED.

SWING. ARM EXTENDED, POINT WITH FINGER IN DIRECTION OF SWING OF BOOM.

MOVE SLOWLY. USE ONE HAND TO GIVE ANY MOTION SIGNAL AND PLACE OTHER HAND MOTIONLESS IN FRONT OF HAND GIVING SIGNAL. (HOIST SLOWLY AS SHOWN IN EXAMPLE.)

STOP. ARM EXTENDED, PALM DOWN, HOLD POSITION RIGIDLY.

EMERGENCY STOP. BOTH ARMS EXTENDED, PALMS DOWN. MOVE BOTH ARMS RAPIDLY BACK AND FORTH HORIZONTALLY.

USE MAIN HOIST. TAP FIST ON HEAD; THEN USE REGULAR SIGNALS.

USE WHIPLINE. (AUXILIARY HOIST). TAP ELBOW WITH ONE HAND; THEN USE REGULAR SIGNALS.

DOG EVERYTHING. (HOLD ALL MOTION). CLASP HANDS IN FRONT OF BODY.

TRAVEL. ARM EXTENDED FORWARD, HAND OPEN AND SLIGHTLY RAISED, MAKE PUSHING MOTION IN DIRECTION OF TRAVEL.

TRAVEL (BOTH TRACKS). BOTH FISTS IN FRONT OF BODY, USING A CIRCULAR MOTION TO INDICATE DIRECTION OF TRAVEL. (FOR LAND CRANES ONLY.)

TRAVEL (ONE TRACK). LOCK TRACK ON SIDE INDICATED BY RAISED FIST. TRAVEL OPPOSITE TRACK IN DIRECTION INDICATED BY CIRCULAR MOTION OF OTHER FIST.

Glossary

A

alloy: Metal formulated from the combination of two or more elements.

asymmetrical load: A load in which one half of the load is substantially different from the other half.

B

bending efficiency: The ratio of the strength of a bent rope to its nominal strength rating.

bend ratio: The ratio of the diameter of a bend to the nominal diameter of the rope.

bevel gear drive: A pair of gears that mesh at an angle, usually 90°.

bight: A loose or slack part of a rope between two fixed ends.

bird caging: A type of damage to wire rope where the outer strands separate and open.

blackwall hitch: A hitch that secures a rope to a hoisting hook.

block: An assembly of one or more pulleys in a frame.

boom: A long beam that projects out from the main part of a crane in order to extend the reach of the hoist.

bowline knot: A knot that forms a loop that is fixed in size.

braiding: The weaving of three or more untwisted strands into a rope.

C

cab: A compartment or platform attached to the crane from which an operator may ride.

cantilever: A projecting structure supported at only one end.

cat's-paw hitch: A hitch used as a quickly formed, light-duty eye.

center of gravity: The balancing point of a load.

chain: A series of metal links connected to one another to form a continuous line.

choke angle: The angle between the vertical component of a choker hitch and the component that surrounds the load.

choker hook: A sliding hook used to form a choker sling when hooked to a sling eye.

clove hitch: A hitch used to secure a rope temporarily to an object.

code: A collection of regulations related to a particular trade or environment.

corrosion: The disintegration of a material due to chemical reaction with its environment.

cow hitch: A hitch composed of a pair of half hitches formed in opposing directions.

crane: A combination of a hoist with a structure to support and move a load.

crossover: A rope wrap winding on top of the preceding wrap.

crowning: A splice that finishes a rope end by braiding its loose strands back on itself.

D

dead end: The loose end of a rope arranged in a loop.

double-hitch knot: A knot composed of two half-hitch knots.

drum: A cylinder on the output of a hoist that rope is wound onto or unwound from.

E

electric hoist: A power-operated hoist that includes an electric motor to provide the input torque to the gear drive.

end truck: A roller assembly consisting of a frame, wheels, and bearings.

eyebolt: A bolt with a looped head that is fastened to a load to provide a lift point.

eye loop: A splice that forms a loop at the end of a rope.

F

fabrication efficiency: The ratio of the tensile strength of a webbing material to the tensile strength of the web sling it is fabricated into.

foundry hook: A hook with a wide, deep throat that fits the handles of molds or castings.

fracture: A crack in metal caused by the stress and fatigue of repeated pulling or bending forces.

G

gantry crane: An industrial crane composed of a bridge beam supported on legs.

grab hook: A hook that can engage and securely hold a chain link.

H

half-hitch knot: A knot where the working end is laid over the standing part and passed through the loop from the opposite side.

hand-chain hoist: A manually operated hoist that uses a continuous hand chain to provide the input torque to the gear drive.

headroom: The distance from the cup of a hoist's top hook to the cup of the hoist hook when the hoist hook is at its upper limit of travel.

hitch: The binding of rope to another object, usually temporarily.

hoist: A mechanical device used to provide the lifting force on lead lines.

hoist hook: A hook with a rounded shape that is suitable for most rigging and lifting applications.

hook: A curved implement used for temporarily connecting rigging to loads or lifting equipment.

hook drift: The continued travel of a hoist hook caused by insufficient motor braking.

I

industrial crane: An indoor crane with permanent structural beam supports.

J

jib crane: An industrial crane that is composed of a cantilevered horizontal beam supported by a single structural leg.

K

kinking: A sharp bend that permanently deforms the lay of rope strands.

knot: The interlacing of a part of a rope to itself, which is then drawn tight.

L

lang-lay rope: A rope in which the yarn or wires and strands are laid in the same direction.

lattice-boom crane: A crane with a boom constructed from a gridwork of steel reinforcing members.

lay: 1. A designation for the direction in which the strands are twisted, specified as they spiral away from the observer. **2.** The length of rope in which a strand makes one complete spiral wrap.

lead line: The part of the rope to which force is applied to hold or move a load.

left-lay rope: A rope with strands that spiral to the left (counterclockwise).

lever-operated hoist: A manually operated hoist that uses the movement of a lever to provide the input torque to the gear drive.

lift: The distance between a hoist's upper and lower limits of travel.

lifting: The hoisting of loads by mechanical means.

lifting lug: A thick metal loop welded or fastened to a load to provide a lift point.

limit switch: A device that activates when a moving component reaches the normal end of travel.

live end: The load-lifting portion of a rope arranged in a loop.

loop: The folding or doubling of a line to create an opening through which another line may pass.

loop eye: A length of webbing folded back and spliced to the sling body, forming a closed loop.

M

manually operated hoist: A hoist that provides mechanical advantage and safety features but relies on a manual force to provide the input torque.

master link: A continuous link used to gather multiple slings and connect them to lift hooks.

mechanical advantage: The ratio of the output force from a machine to the input force applied.

mobile crane: A crane that can be moved between job sites.

N

nip: A pressure point created when a rope crosses over itself after a turn around an object.

nominal value: A designated value that may vary slightly from the actual value.

O

outrigger: An extendable support structure that increases a crane's footprint in order to improve stability.

overhead crane: An industrial crane that is composed of a bridge beam assembly that travels along a pair of overhead beams.

P

part: A rope length between a hook and block or between two blocks.

pendant: A pushbutton or lever control suspended from a hoist or crane.

plaiting: The weaving of four pairs of alternately twisted strands into a rope.

pneumatic hoist: A power-operated hoist that uses an air motor to provide the input torque to the gear drive.

pocket wheel: A sprocket-like wheel with chain-link pockets.

power-operated hoist: A hoist operated by a power source that is controlled by an operator.

preformed rope: A wire rope in which the strands are permanently formed into a helical shape during fabrication.

R

ratchet: A mechanism in which a toothed wheel is prevented from turning backwards by engagement with a spring-loaded pawl.

reach: The distance between the cup of the top hook and the cup of the hoist hook when the hoist hook is at its lower limit of travel.

reel: A wooden cylinder on which rope is wound for shipping and storage.

reeving: The passing of a rope through an opening or around a pulley.

regular-lay rope: A rope in which the yarn or wires in the strands are twisted in the opposite direction of the lay of the strands.

regulation: A rule made mandatory by a federal, state, or local government.

rigging: the securing of loads with the proper equipment and arrangement in preparation for lifting.

right-lay rope: A rope with strands that spiral to the right (clockwise).

rope: A length of fibers or thin wires that are twisted or braided together to form a strong and flexible line.

round sling: An endless (continuous loop) sling consisting of unwoven synthetic fiber yarns enclosed in a protective cover.

runway: A rail and beam combination.

S

safety factor: The ratio of a component's ultimate strength to its maximum allowable safe working load limit.

scaffold hitch: A hitch used to hang or support planks or beams.

seizing: The wire wrapping that binds the end of a wire rope near where it is cut.

selvedge: An edge treatment on woven material that prevents unraveling.

shackle: A U-shaped metal connector with holes drilled into the ends for receiving a removable pin or bolt.

sling: A line used to lift, lower, or carry a load.

sling angle: The angle between the horizontal and the sling.

sling hitch: A sling arrangement that has a loop at both ends to rig a load for lifting.

slip clutch: A spring-loaded, friction-held fiber disc that is adjusted to slip at 125% to 150% of the hoist's rated load.

slip knot: A knot that can slip along the standing part of a rope to tighten a loop.

socket: A rope attachment through which a rope end is terminated.

sorting hook: A hook with a straight, tapered tip that can be used to directly hold plates, cylinders, and other shapes that allow full engagement.

spelter socket: A socket that uses molten zinc or resin to secure the end of a wire rope inside the socket.

splice: 1. The braiding together of two portions of rope in order to form a permanent connection. **2.** An overlap of webbing material that is sewn together.

standard: A collection of voluntary rules developed through consensus and related to a particular trade, industry, or environment.

standing end: The end of the standing part.

standing part: The portion of a rope that is unaltered or not involved in making a knot or hitch.

strand: Several pieces of yarn or wire twisted spirally around an axis.

swage socket: A socket that is compressed onto the end of a wire rope.

symmetrical load: A load in which one half of the load is a mirror image of the other half.

T

tackle: The combination of ropes and accessories arranged with blocks to gain mechanical advantage for lifting.

tag line: A rope, handled by an individual, to control rotational movement of a load during lifting.

telescopic-boom crane: A crane with an extendable boom composed of nested sections.

thimble: A curved piece of metal around which a rope is fitted to form a loop.

timber hitch: A hitch used to wrap and drag lengthy material.

torque: Rotational force.

tuck set: The wedging of a strand into and between two other rope strands.

U

unlay: The untwisting of the strands in a rope.

W

wagoner's hitch knot: A knot that provides a taunt line with a 3:1 mechanical advantage.

wear pad: A leather or webbed pad used to protect the web sling from damage.

webbing: Flat narrow strapping woven from yarns of strong synthetic fibers.

web sling: A flat rigging sling made from synthetic webbing material.

web sling body: The portion of the sling that is between the loop eyes or end fittings (if any).

web sling length: The distance between the ends of a web sling, including any fittings.

wedge socket: A socket that holds a loop of wire rope securely with a wedge that is tightened by tension on the rope.

whipping: The twine wrapping that binds the end of a fiber rope near where it is cut.

working end: The end of the working part.

working load limit: The maximum weight that a rigging component may be subjected to.

working part: The portion of the rope involved in making the knot.

worm gear drive: A pair of gears consisting of a spiral-threaded worm (drive gear) and a worm wheel (driven gear).

Y

yarn: A continuous line of fibers twisted together.

Index

Page numbers in italic refer to figures.